The Stress Barrier
Nature's Way to Overcoming Stress

About the author

Dr Pradeep Chadha is currently practising as a psychotherapist and stress management consultant. He is a trained psychiatrist and hypnotherapist. His special interest is in the drugless management of stress-related mental disorders.

If you wish to avail of Dr Chadha's professional services please feel free to contact him directly.

Dr Pradeep K Chadha
Rhodes Consultants Ltd
48 Upper Drumcondra Road
Dublin 9
Tel: 00-353-1-857-1145
e-mail: chadhap@rhodes.ie

The Stress Barrier

Nature's Way to Overcoming Stress

Dr Pradeep K Chadha

MBBS DCP DPM (RCPI & RCSI)
Fellow of the American Institute of Stress

BLACKHALL
Publishing

This book was typeset by Red Dot for

BLACKHALL PUBLISHING
26 Eustace Street
Dublin 2
Ireland

e-mail: blackhall@tinet.ie

ISBN: 1 901657 65 5 pbk

A catalogue record for this book is available from the British Library.

Printed in Ireland by
Betaprint Ltd

Contents

Acknowledgements x
Foreword xi
Introduction xiii

PART 1: NATURE'S ROLE IN LIFE – AN INTRODUCTION

1. Nature's Role in Life 3
    - working with nature 3
    - acceptance and respect 4
    - seen and unseen ways of nature 5
    - ways to learn 7
    - emotions and their validation in medicine 8
    - the animate and inanimate worlds 9

2. Nature and its Principles 11
    - the principle of freedom of choice 11
    - the principle of balances 12
    - the principle of least effort 16
    - the principle of temporariness 17
    - the principle of cause and effect 18
    - the principle of life and death 18
    - the principle of responsibility for self 21
    - the spiritual basis of life 24

PART 2: THE STRESSED STATE

3. The Physiological Basis of Stress 33
    - feedback mechanisms 33
    - the role of the nervous system 34
    - the role of neurotransmitters 38
    - the role of emotions 39
    - defining stress 41
    - what is stress? 41
    - neurotransmitters and stress 42
    - physical and mental stress 43
    - stressors 44
    - conditioning and stress 49
    - theory of relativity and stress 51
    - the mind-body connection in stress 51

4. The Effects of Stress **55**
- perception, thinking, behaviour, emotion 55
- emotions and stress 58
- stress and personality 59
- higher brain and lower brain 60
- the cycle of stress 61
- the cycle of de-stress or the cycle of positivity 63
- emotions, stress and psychotherapy 64
- stress and Nature's principles 65
- signs of stress 68
- stress is infectious 73
- how we can diminish stress 75
- how stress affects our memory 76

5. The Long-term Effects of Stress **79**
- physical and psychosomatic illness 80
- mental illness 81
- addictions 81
- weight problems and eating disorders 84
- abuse 86
- complaining and blaming 87
- obsessions 87
- child rearing 88
- religious and political fanaticism 90
- racism 91
- affairs in the workplace 91
- family life 92
- decision-making 92
- corruption 93
- the relationship between stress and de-stress 94
- the words we use 98
- advantages of stress 100

PART 3: THE DE-STRESSED STATE

6. Long-term Effects of a De-stressed State **103**
- accumulated effects 105
- spirituality and the de-stressed state 105
- acceptance 106
- open-mindedness 106
- abundance 106
- wisdom 107
- self-discipline 107

- freedom of spirit 107
- adaptability 108
- humility 108
- physical and mental health 108
- optimism and positive thinking 109
- growth.. 109
- slowed ageing 110
- signs of a de-stressed state..................................... 110

7. Achieving a De-stressed State **117**
- slowing down and stopping.................................... 118
- resources for de-stressing 119
- exposure to long-term stress................................... 119
- exposure to short-term stress................................. 120
- the active process... 120
- having a holiday every day of our lives.................... 121
- a de-stressed state in an individual and a system 122
- the basis of de-stressing techniques....................... 123
- how physical exercise reduces individual stress 124
- the role of the senses 124
- economical ways of de-stressing ourselves........................... 129
- stress and the law... 131
- the final word.. 131

8. Exercises.. **133**

Bibliography... 141

Index.. 143

Dedication

He, who is known by different names in different ages.
My guide, master and teacher.
Mr Harbans Lal Bhambri
Mrs Shobha Bhambri (who passed away during the publication of this book).

ACKNOWLEDGEMENTS

I would like to extend thankful appreciation to Patricia Ford and Gráinne Murphy for their secretarial support. I would also like to thank Nick Mulcahy, Tony Mason and Gerry O'Connor for their encouragement in producing this book. Finally, I am thankful to my clients and my family for making this project possible.

Pradeep K Chadha

September 1999

FOREWORD

The subject of stress has become a big issue in business circles, and in society at large, in the late 20th Century. It has spawned a plethora of books on the topic, massive media coverage, and a large number of legal cases, as workers affected by stress seek redress in the courts. Sums as high as £175,000 have been awarded in the British courts to employees who have suffered mental breakdown as a result of work-related stress.

While there have been many books on stress and the management of stress, they have in the main tended to look at the subject in isolation, rather than seeing stress and stress-related problems as part of the flow of life. This is where Pradeep Chadha's book is different, in that it is the first book to seriously consider the spiritual, scientific and social aspects of stress. The book acknowledges that there is more to stress than mental and external factors, and that people will not solve their stress-related problems by, for example, taking less work home, or cutting difficult colleagues out of their life. These actions may help to ease the problem, but they will only be a temporary solution. Stress is a more fundamental problem than that and as such it requires more far-reaching and holistic solutions.

Very few of the books written on this subject to date deal in anything other than a cursory manner with crucially important issues such as meditation, relaxation, psychology and medication, and even fewer explore the fundamental links between these areas. I commend Dr Chadha's book because it does deal with these issues and also because it does not shy away from the importance of spirituality and the basic laws of nature when considering stress.

The book, like Dr Chadha's consultancy work, is presented in an accessible, step-by-step fashion, and the reader is given a series of simple exercises which will help them to identify, and start to overcome, their particular stress-related problems.

Overall, this is a valuable contribution to the literature currently available on stress, and I have no hesitation in wholeheartedly endorsing it and recommending it to the reader.

Dr Ivor Browne
FRCPI, FRCPsych., DPM, MSc (Harv)
Consultant Psychiatrist
Professor Emeritus
September 1999

INTRODUCTION

When the wisest student hears about the Tao
He follows it without ceasing
When the average student hears about it
He follows too, but not all the time...
And when the poor student gets wind of it
He laughs at it like an idiot!
And if he didn't, then it wouldn't be the Tao.

The Tao Te Ching

This book is divided into four parts. Each part can be read independently or the parts can be read in conjunction with one another.

The first part of the book deals with some basic concepts of life. We usually tend to ignore these concepts because they seem insignificant. These concepts are like alphabets of a language. When we have mastered a language, we consciously forget the existence of alphabets. Only when we lose our power to speak or hear, does the knowledge of alphabets become significant. We then have to communicate by writing words with these alphabets. We may have to write laborious notes at such times. The first part of the book makes us aware of such alphabets in natural operations, which we ignore – often end up stressed out.

The second part of the book is about stress in general. An attempt has been made to cover as much ground as possible by looking at stress from various perspectives. It is linked to the first part of the book. In this part, we look at how stress is generated by flouting Nature's principles.

The third part of the book deals with background information about how we can de-stress ourselves. It is an attempt to understand stress more fully and contains ideas and cues to newer techniques that we may be able to develop on our own. This knowledge can be applied to de-stress various aspects of our life.

The fourth part of the book is actually spread out throughout the three parts. It consists of thought provoking concepts and ideas. The exercises in the final chapter have been applied clinically many times and are very effective. Some of them are powerful enough to bring about changes in minutes. As such, they need to be approached with caution by people with an illness of any kind. Advice from a doctor should be taken in such cases.

In the book, I have used terms such as 'brain' and 'mind' or 'relaxation' and 'de-stress', which are interchangeable terms. Anticipating the fast pace of life of readers, each section of the book, though linked with other parts, can be read on its own. So even if you have a few minutes to spare, you can dip into any page of the book and get something out of it. Enjoy the book!

PART 1
NATURE'S ROLE IN LIFE –
AN INTRODUCTION

1. NATURE'S ROLE IN LIFE

Once upon a time, there lived a king in Central Asia. He was too ambitious. He wanted to be richer than other kings. He had heard that India was a rich country. People were prosperous. There was plenty of gold and precious stones in the country. The king attacked India for her riches. He took away whatever gold, jewellery and precious stones he could take away. For it, he had to kill many people. He made many people unhappy with his ambitions.

He attacked India, again and again – a total of seventeen times. His ambition and greed were unsatiated. On his deathbed, he ordered his subjects to gather all the wealth he had mustered in his life. There were heaps of jewellery, gold coins and precious stones and many animals. The king looked at all of this – and cried. He could not take anything with him into his next life after death. He died an unhappy man. Had he been slightly more secure in himself, a little more de-stressed, he could have lived a happier man.

*Stress is about fighting with natural forces, without any necessity for it. Stress creates in us fear, insecurity and greed – like the king in the story. It makes us unhappy and generates unhappiness around us. Fortunately, there **are** ways to work **with** Nature, by having **inside** knowledge. Though all of us can develop the ability to gain this knowledge, very few of us have the patience for it.*

Working with Nature

Nature is more powerful than any individual. In fact it is more powerful than the whole of mankind put together. It is more powerful than the galaxies and universe put together. Nature looks after billions and trillions of organisms on Earth alone. At this moment in time there are around five billion human beings on this planet. Each human being consists of trillions of cells. Each cell is a living being that Nature looks after. Nature looks after each organism from the time of its birth to the time of its death. Yet some of us decide to fight Nature when difficulties arise for us.

Fighting Nature is a dangerous game. We might win; we might lose. Even if we win, the effects of fighting with Nature have an impact on other areas of our life. For example, when we have a fever due to an infection, we tend to deal with the infection and the fever using medications. Although fighting infection and controlling fever helps the body to live, the side effects of the drugs leave us weak immunologically and physically. If we accept that fever is a manifestation of the infection and is there to help the individual to survive, things become easier for us. In actual fact, fever, which means increased temperature of the body, is detrimental to the infecting organism. Using this fever to help us to fight infection is one way of working with Nature. The other way is to construe fever as something harmful, which it would be, if the temperature goes up to the extent that body proteins become denatured. But if we take fever as a symptom, which we have to fight irrespective of how low the fever is, we fight with Nature once again, bringing more side effects to a body, which is already fighting infections. It is sometimes (maybe most of the time) wiser to work *with* Nature. We have limited capabilities to understand when and how to work with Nature. **Working with Nature is obviously more rewarding than fighting with it.**

> **FOOD FOR THOUGHT**
> Nature operates to provide us with our needs. When our 'wants' become 'needs', forces of Nature back us up to enable us to fulfil our 'need'.

Acceptance and Respect

When we accept any fact we spontaneously develop a respect for it. Respecting someone means accepting someone. When we respect the president of our country, we accept the person as the president of our country. When we accept a person as the president of our country, we can respect that person as the president of our country. Non-acceptance and disrespect cause most of life's struggles and stresses. Acceptance and respect are very closely linked. If we respect ourselves, it becomes very easy to respect others – and it happens spontaneously. When we respect ourselves as capable of doing something, we also *accept* the fact that we have that capability. Life becomes easy knowing our capabilities and respecting them. It enables us to perform to our full potential. **When we respect ourselves and accept ourselves the way we are, it becomes easy to accept others and respect others spontaneously and unconditionally.**

> **FOOD FOR THOUGHT**
> Our 'needs' - like air and water - are freely available in Nature. We create 'wants' and pay for them.

Respecting Nature and accepting whatever comes our way is a significant move towards helping ourselves deal with Nature. We can deal with Nature without necessarily fighting it. If we accept that fighting, as violence, is the last resort for dealing with any problem, respecting Nature becomes very easy. When we respect Nature it enables us to work along with it. When Nature works with us, there is a manifold increase in our energies, because we are tapping into those unseen resources that push us to move forward in life.

Seen and Unseen Ways of Nature

Nature acts through seen and unseen ways. We see the white light of the sun. We can see the seven colours of this white light using a prism. Only by using a prism or something like a prism, can we know that this white light is composed of seven colours. Therefore, even though light helps us to see objects, we cannot see light with our own eyes.

On the two sides of the spectrum, there are waves that are not seen by the naked eye. These rays fall into the range of ultraviolet and infrared rays. We can experience these rays in various forms. Standing in front of a x-ray machine and getting a picture of our internal structure reveals to us that x-rays are capable of passing through our body. We do not see these rays. Microwaves are used to cook food. We cannot *see* these waves with the naked eye. We can only experience them when the food is cooked. We experience heat energy as a result of passing microwaves through any food item that contains water. Until a few years ago, from any sane person's point of view, these rays did not exist. No one had seen these rays or experienced their effect.

Air cannot be seen. Only in comparatively recent times has it been scientifically proven that air is matter and that air has weight. But air existed even before we had these proofs. We continue to breathe in this air as did our ancestors, with or without this knowledge. They were still breathing in oxygen, and breathing out carbon dioxide without giving names to these gases.

There have been in Nature phenomena, that we haven't understood at any given moment in time. We can however, experience these phenomena. With time and in time as man's curiosity develops this knowledge unfolds itself. Once again it is Nature that decides when to reveal that knowledge. There are many phenomena especially pertaining to the mind and the brain that we are still fascinated about. We are still unclear on many issues as to how certain things happen, such as how certain thinking processes, emotions and behaviours affect various aspects of life. We have still to learn many things. Whenever Nature decides to

Diagram A: Using a prism to see the seven colours of sunlight

White light is a combination of seven colours. These colours of the spectrum can be seen when the white light is passed through a prism. Similar 'special conditions' can be created to 'see' the 'invisible' around us.

reveal this knowledge to us, it will come to us. Our job is to continue seeking. If we stop seeking, we stop learning. Nature will cease to be generous to us. We need to continue to look for answers, bearing in mind that there are methods of how to look for answers and how to get those answers and that many of these methods are unscientific.

Ways to Learn

We live in an age of science. Science has a standard, a way of asking questions. The most interesting thing about scientific learning is that it is man-made. We learn what we want to learn, the way we want to learn. Every few years some people sit together in some part of the world and decide about the 'scientific method'. If there is anything that does not meet that man-made scientific standard, it is rejected, whereas anything that meets that standard is accepted. Such knowledge would consist of facts that are seen to be happening or existing. **Anything that cannot be seen but can be felt through senses goes beyond scientific evidences.** Such phenomena are many times harder to validate or duplicate, even if conditions are similar.

The limitation of scientific evidence is that we start to learn a phenomenon from a pre-conceived notion that such a phenomenon may or may not occur. We eventually conclude that something that we were looking for scientifically occurs or does not occur. What we miss learning in the process is the vast knowledge that is beyond that particular scientific fact that we are trying to validate. As we are looking for only one particular point to learn, we miss hundreds and thousands of other points related to the same subject that we fail to observe and learn as a consequence. However, science still has to find ways and means to measure, to validate phenomena, processes that can only be felt with the senses.

Most of the patients coming into psychiatric services, when asked what is happening with their lives, want to know why a particular illness is affecting them. Some say, "I want to know why I am suffering with depression" whereas others ask, "Why is this happening to me?"

The first questions to ask in this situation start with a 'what' rather than with a why: "What is happening to me?", "What is the pattern of what is happening to me?" The next questions that arise are, "How can I change this pattern?" or "What can I do to change this pattern?" Once these questions are answered, the problem can be negotiated successfully most of the time. Once we can negotiate the problem and emerge successfully, we spontaneously get the answer to the question 'why'.

The answer to the question 'why' comes last. If we start with the wrong question, how can we possibly get the right answer?

This phenomenon of looking at the pattern and getting answers to 'whats' and 'hows' has been successfully used in many forms of therapy. If Newton had been looking for the answer as to "why has the apple fallen" on his head, he would have probably fought with the apple and worried about it for the rest of his life. Instead he looked at the whole process and studied the 'what' aspect of it – what happens that makes the apple fall. This was probably the way he started getting his answers. **The way to proceed to find the answer to a problem is by looking at the process and starting with 'what' as a first step.**

Emotions and their Validation in Medicine

Emotions are said to be the result of the activities of the old brain, also known as the primitive brain or the instinctual brain. The higher brain, called the intelligent brain or the cognitive brain, is said to control these instincts. This old brain, a part of which is called the limbic system, controls our emotions, instincts and other biological needs, including the need to survive. One of the most interesting facts of psychiatry is that functional mental illnesses, which form a significant proportion of psychiatric service consumption, occur due to emotional problems. Feelings of sadness, grief, anger and fear are very quickly given scientific, psychiatric labels by us, because we can validate them. We look at the physical symptoms of the effects of these emotional problems and also their effects on brain activity and, based on the behavioural and physiological aspects of the effects, we give a scientific diagnosis. And yet the same feelings and emotions can be dealt with in early stages by the simple processes of talking and therapy. Yet in some of the most advanced universities, psychotherapy is being discredited as an ineffective tool of help. In one way it is an interesting development. In many countries of Asia, the word psychotherapy doesn't exist in the same form as it does in the West. The reason for this is that in many Asian countries, all therapy, as we know of it in the West, is done in one's home within the family. Because of the close-knit family structure, any person having emotional difficulties finds a ready outlet in the form of friends and relatives. This helps to clear away difficulties, which could otherwise lead to psychiatric illnesses, as we know of them in the Western world.

The Animate and Inanimate Worlds

Geologists tell us that the petroleum that we get from under the Earth's crust is a result of the organic matter – dead plants and animals - that was buried under the Earth's crust thousands of years ago. In other words, plants and animals that were living thousands of years ago are now used as petrol, a fuel. Fuel gives us energy. It means that the animate matter that was once alive has been converted into energy. Wise people have been saying for centuries that energy and matter are interchangeable.

Fossils are the solidified remains of old plants and animals. Some of the tree fossils are so old that with time they have been converted into stones. Some of the fish, including species that have become extinct, have been discovered under the earth's crust in solidified forms, often as stones. Stones, as rock, can thus be formed from once living matter. Similarly, we could be available to future generations as fuel or stones. (It is probably a hard fact to swallow, to imagine becoming petroleum or stone, but scientific evidence shows that this is what happens in Nature).

Einstein put forward a hypothesis that energy and matter are inter-convertible. Matter can be converted to energy and energy can be converted to matter. Going through old literature from each and every civilisation, we come across writings that have repeatedly reminded us that matter and energy are inter-convertible. Some of these cultures have used terms like God, Allah, Omm, as energy forms that provide life forms on this Earth and maybe elsewhere. In some of the old literature it is evidently written that Nature, or God, or whatever name we may call it, is a form of energy which some describe as light, others describe as sound.

> *In the beginning was the word and the word was God.*
> *New Testament John 1:1*

It has been written again and again that every life form and every inanimate form is a manifestation of that energy. Many religions have also mentioned that God is a form of energy that exists in all of us. These literatures also say that all of us have part of God within us. Conversion of energy into matter and matter into energy is a game that Nature has played in the universe since the beginning of time. The game continues to be played and will be played in the future. **Matter and energy will continue to be converted from one form into the other whether we believe in it or not, or whether we have scientific evidence for it or**

not. But we do know from science now that matter and energy can neither be created nor destroyed.

From ashes to ashes, from dust to dust.

This line is very familiar to people in the Christian world. This one line exposes one of the greatest truths of Nature. We, who are animate, are made from inanimate objects.

We, in time, will get converted into inanimate elements and objects again. This could be a very hard truth for some to swallow. But it is the truth. This may also mean that all animate or inanimate objects interchange their positions and places in time. This is probably the reason why all spiritual beliefs remind us again and again that everything in this Nature deserves the respect that we give to the Lord God. In old Vedic literature, every living form, even that of single-celled animals is believed to be a form of God. This is the basis of the belief in vegetarianism.

FOOD FOR THOUGHT
If each of us was to take responsibility for our own happiness, growth and well being, we could spontaneously contribute the same to the society around us.

2.   NATURE AND ITS PRINCIPLES

Nature operates on numerous laws and principles. Many of them we already know. For example, there is darkness when it is night, and there is a cycle of night and day. Similarly, for every living organism, there is a predisposing seed or some source, from which the organism will begin life. It could be called a spore, an egg, a sperm, a seed or whatever. We have yet to create life from non-life. If and when we do that, we would have solved the mystery of how life began. Broadly speaking, for every life form there has to be a source of life that gives birth to it.

Another of Nature's laws is that whoever is born is bound to grow old with time. We might be able to slow down ageing in the future with the help of science, but we will still have to age. This is the law of nature. Similarly, time moves forward and cannot go backward. This is another law.

These are some of the laws that we know of, that we have been able to prove scientifically. There are many other laws that we either ignore or are hidden from our observation because they are very fine, like the small print on a contract form. These laws and principles are constantly in operation. They have always been there and they will always be there as long as there is life on earth. We know some of these laws and some of the laws are hidden from our view. Listed below are some of these laws. Knowledge of these laws can make life easier for us, as once we know the laws, we can observe them. We also learn what happens when these laws are broken and what happens when these laws are followed. **Being aware of these laws gives us an advantage as they help ourselves work with Nature.** Nature is such a powerful force that if we work with it, it pushes us all to great heights in a very short time and if we oppose it, it destroys us. These laws of Nature probably operate at every level of the universe. They operate from the lowest level of life to the highest physical levels that we know of – the earth, the solar system and the galaxy.

The Principle of Freedom of Choice

According to this principle, we have the freedom to choose many aspects of our life. Not only can we choose our partners, but we can also determine many aspects of our life, which we would usually see as being beyond our control. People unconsciously choose to lead a particular kind of lifestyle and end up achieving their goals. It is the kind of choice we make that determines what we have, what we get, what we do with our own lives.

Hitler, with whatever qualifications he had, made the choice that he had to rule Germany one day. He made the choice and he did what he wanted to do. As his ambitions grew, his choice was to rule the whole of Europe. In order to do that he had to stake the security of Germany and his own personal security. Once his choice was made, he destroyed himself.

At many times in our life we have to make choices. We make these choices and sometimes find that they cannot be put into action immediately. We then have a feeling that they are probably not going to be fulfilled. But Nature operates as if it registers the choices that we make and many times these choices are fulfilled.

Scientific research has shown that if someone decides that they want to commit suicide, they end up doing just that. On the other hand, if someone wants to commit suicide because he or she believes that there is no way out, then it is a choice that the person makes. But as soon as the person chooses to get help for suicidal thoughts, Nature starts helping the person in that direction. Clinically, I have come across many such people, who even though they were going through the worst periods of their lives, decided that they needed help of some sort. It was very interesting to observe that they did get help from unexpected sources. They helped themselves by making their initial choice, which changed the direction of their lives. Many criminal minds have similarly made the choice that they want to make a career in crime. Their choice is dutifully respected by Nature.

The Principle of Balances

This is one of the most important principles of Nature. At each and every stage in life, at each and every stage in history, at each and every step that we take, there needs to be a balance between opposing forces. In various literatures, at various times, there has been an emphasis put on 'balance'. This balance between two opposing forces, usually, has been described as between Yin and Yang in spiritual literature, between positivity and negativity in electricity, between materialism and spirituality in philosophy, between mind and body in health, between too much and too little in every aspect of our lives. To create a balance in our lives is one of the most difficult things to do. It is also one of the most important things for us to do. Having a balance in our life makes us happy and stress-free. An imbalance in our lives makes us feel stress, which makes us unhappy.

A classical example of 'balance' is 'wave motion'. In physics we learn how a wave is generated.

A wave is generated when a particle is pushed by a neighbouring particle. This happens in upward and downward motion alternately. The particle is pushed upwards to an 'extreme' limit forming a crest. Subsequently, it is pushed downwards to reach its lowest point. The direction of the waveform is horizontal.

Sound waves are created by alternate contraction and expansion of air particles.

Once again, these two extremes, between which, when air particles (or any other medium) move, sound is produced. At each and every step in life, in every activity, there are extremes, between which, we need to maintain a balance. Too much or too little of anything are two extremes. Somewhere between them is the balance.

Balance is what Nature provides, in various forms. On the one hand Nature creates, and on the other hand it destroys. Life and death are two examples of this balance. Hypothetically speaking, if all of the people who have been born on this earth were still alive today the population of this earth would be manifold. Let us keep in mind that most of those people alive still could be reproducing. Nature has kept its balance with death. In recent years there have been advancements in medicine, which have ensured that we have longer lives. As a result, the population of the world has increased. Nature will find some way to balance this overgrowing population.

Some recent examples of natural catastrophes, which have been stalled by mankind, were AIDS and CJD. We have been successful in limiting the damage these two diseases could have done. These were recent attempts by Nature to undo the imbalance created by the present overpopulation in the world. In fact, scientists now tell us that the male human beings have a smaller number of sperms per millilitre of semen compared to their counterparts a century ago. This is probably another way in which nature is creating a balance. Added to this phenomenon is the current trend of late marriages and decreasing fertility in women. Nature has a tendency to find its balance some way.

Balance is the key to life. A balanced life is a happy and prosperous life. If there is poverty, there is an imbalance in one's life. If there is no peace of mind, there is an imbalance in one's life. If there is stress of any kind, there is an imbalance in one's life. If there is any illness, there is an imbalance in one's life. Imbalance

FOOD FOR THOUGHT
Work, from Nature's perspective, is regularity without pushing ourselves too hard.

Diagram B: A Wave Motion

DIRECTION OF WAVE

CREST

TROUGH

MEAN

UPPER EXTREME

LOWER EXTREME

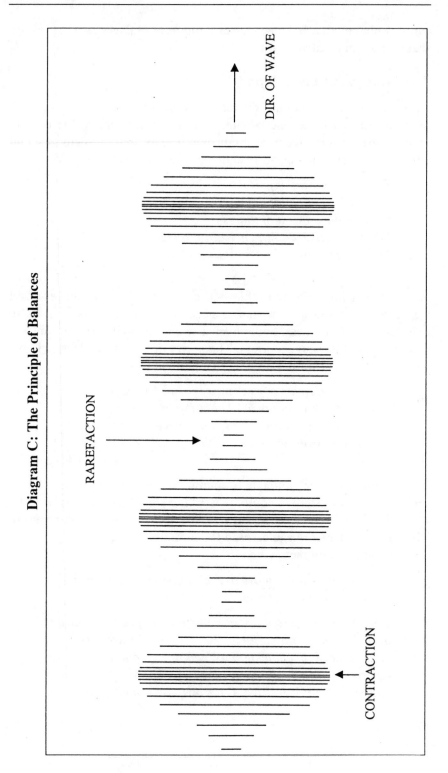

Diagram C: The Principle of Balances

causes unhappiness. Balance causes happiness. Balance is what Nature seeks, and what it always gets.

The Principle of Least Effort

According to this principle, we require very little effort to do most of the things in our lives. The simplest way to do anything in life usually requires least effort. Because of our own insecurities we seem to spend a lot of our energy and effort to achieve what we want to achieve.

> *The very softest thing of all*
> *can ride like a galloping horse*
> *through the hardest of things.*
> *Like water, like water penetrating rock.*
> *And so the invisible enters in.*
>
> *Tao Te Ching*

We need very little effort to achieve great things in life. Whatever effort we spend over and above what is needed is a waste. This results in exhaustion and tiredness, both physically and mentally. This strains the systems and puts us under stress. The secret of this principle is to know what is the least effort required to do a particular job.

> *The Tao of Heaven doesn't struggle, but wins through.*
> *It doesn't ask yet it always hears the answer –*
> *It doesn't demand yet things come, because they want to*
> *It has no desires and yet everything works out as planned.*
>
> *Tao Te Ching*

This means that in any animate or inanimate system, very little effort is required for the system to continue working smoothly and survive. **The less effort a system uses to survive the more energy is conserved.** This conserved energy can be used for further growth.

Newton's law on inertia states:

> *A body continues to move at the same speed in a particular direction until an external force acts on it.*

> *A body continues to move at a particular speed in a particular direction without force, without any disturbance. This is a natural phenomenon. When interfered with by an external force, only then does its speed or direction change. This is also true of our own lives in general.*

The Principle of Temporariness

According to this principle, everything in this universe changes. This means that everything in life changes. If we look around ourselves and remember the years that we have spent on this earth, we would realise that things are different from the time we were born. Although the sun and the moon have continued to rise and set day after day, month after month, year after year, everything else has changed. Wise people have stated that only death and God are certainties in this world. These two are permanent.

> *The changes that appear to occur in the empty world*
> *we call real only because of our ignorance.*
>
> *Teachings of the Buddha*

There are many moments in our life when we feel desperate, even hopeless. At such moments we feel as if the world has come to a standstill. But yet everything moves on and everything changes. We pass through difficult times in our lives, and we go into times when we are happy. Moreover, if we look at this happiness, even that changes. **So, happiness and unhappiness are changeable moments in our lives. Acceptance of this fact makes our lives easier.**

Change is an integral part of our lives. It is something inevitable. Hardly anything remains static for long. We might see old buildings, which could be a few hundred years old. We might see old castles and palaces, which might be a thousand years old. But according to this principle of mutability, they *will* come to an end some day. Civilisations have risen, have reached their peaks, and have fallen. There was a Roman Empire once. There was a Greek Empire once. There was an Egyptian civilisation once. Where are they now? They have all changed with time. **What we see today, may not exist tomorrow.**

Today's so-called world powers *will not* be world powers in a few decades. This is inevitable and certain. This is because the mutability that exists in Nature changes everything. There is a system to this. If we attempt to make a system static or stable, it is difficult to maintain this status for a long period of time. The system must move either backwards or forwards. It has to make progress or it has to digress. With time, depending on the nature of the competence of the system, it will either stagnate or destroy itself, or grow and give happiness to others. If we are sad, we can be happy after some time. **Sadness, if allowed to go, never lasts forever.**

The Principle of Cause and Effect

Some people equate the principle of cause and effect with the theory of karma. **According to this principle, for every effect there is a cause and every cause has an effect.** This principle has been used even in therapy. In certain forms of therapy, if you remove an emotional or underlying cause of a problem, then the problem sorts itself out. Many others do not believe that such laws exist and are workable. Whatever the truth, the laws of Nature exist and operate, whether we accept them or not. They affect our lives in many ways whether or not we acknowledge them. The Bible says:

> *As you shall sow, so you shall reap.*

If this is not a cause and effect relationship, then what is it?

Some people are confused by the connection they make between the theory of karma and reincarnation. These people believe that the theory of karma *only* relates to reincarnation. In other words, what we do in this life will be rewarded or punished in the next life. No wonder they also miss the point that the theory of karma is about every cause having an effect and every effect having a cause. We reap only what we sow. In other words, the theory of karma is equal to "as you shall sow, so you shall reap". Is it not possible that we might be getting the cause and effect of happenings in this very life and that we do not have to wait for our next life or lives to get what is due to us? If Nature operates on the principle of cause and effect, then why does it wait till the next life to give us our dues? Why can it not happen within this lifetime here and now? Whatever the truth, the principle of cause and effect seems to operate in some visible forms. If the cause of brightness in the day, the sun, were not there, we would not have had daylight and if the darkness were not there, we would not have had the effect of the night.

In actual fact this principle of cause and effect follows another law of Nature that states that everything in nature follows a cyclical pattern. **Everything in Nature is a part of a cycle: from where we start to where we come to after going through the cycle.**

The Principle of Life and Death

> *Everything that is born has to die,*
> *And everything that dies has to be born.*
> *This is the eternal truth.*
>
> Bhagwad Gita

In Nature there is a particular quantity of water available. This water is in the oceans, seas, rivers, lakes, waterfalls, glaciers, and poles of the

Earth. Every year, every month, every moment, some water vapours from these sources evaporate to form clouds in the sky. The clouds move to somewhere else and, when they become cold, they condense to form water, which falls down to the Earth. This water once again goes back to oceans, to seas, to rivers, to lakes, to glaciers and to the poles. This is a cycle.

Diagram D: The Water Cycle

In botany we are taught about the 'Nitrogen Cycle'. In this cycle, nitrogen that is present in about 80 per cent of the air is used by certain bacteria that are present in the roots of pea and bean plants. In the roots of these plants, known as legumes, there are small nodules of bacteria. These bacteria are available only in the roots of these legumes. A special feature of these bacteria is that they are able to utilise the nitrogen from the air around them to manufacture amino acids, which are converted into proteins. Leguminous plants are the only sources of plant proteins. The next step in the nitrogen cycle occurs when other animals, including human beings, eat the proteins of these plants. These proteins are then digested, assimilated and excreted. The metabolic products of these proteins once again go back to air in the form of gases like ammonia and nitrogen. Once again, we see a cycle of nitrogen starting from the air and coming back to the air.

Diagram E: The Nitrogen Cycle

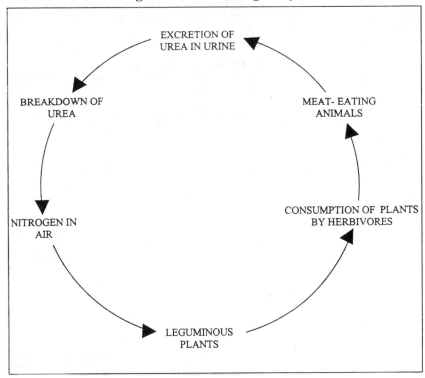

The above are two examples of cycles that occur in Nature. In chemistry we are aware of a law of conservation of matter. This law states that matter can be neither created nor destroyed. In other words, whatever we see of matter in the form of liquids, solids or gases has the ability to change from one form into the other, but the quantity remains the same.

Another physical law states that energy can be neither created nor destroyed. This law is also known as the law of conservation of energy. We can change one form of energy into another. We can change sound into heat, heat into light or light into heat. Whatever we do, the net result is that we are changing one form of energy into another form of energy. We can also split the atom and create energy as a result. One form of matter can be changed into a form of energy. Water can be changed into ice or steam but its destruction is impossible. One form of matter can be changed into another form of matter. In other words, everything in this universe – at least as we know of it – is recycled.

Most of the bigger things in the Universe are round in structure. Almost all planets and other heavenly bodies are round or circular. The sun, the moon and the Earth are circular, for example. The orbits of planets around the sun are circular. The orbit of the moon is round. These movements might be elliptical, but they are still circular. As in any cycle, we come to the same point from where we started, having completed the circle. Maybe there is a message in these circles or cycles, which we have yet to pick up.

In some Eastern cultures, many people believe in life after death. In these cultures people take comparatively little time to grieve over their losses. This belief system makes sure that as they lose their near and dear ones they can say goodbye to them comparatively easily. If everything is recycled then what possibilities do we have of being recycled again in future? This raises many questions, some of which we can answer and some of which remain unanswered. Whatever the truth is, the flow of life and death remains stable in nature. We are born and we die. Whether we are born again is Nature's work and Nature takes its own course. Nature – with whatever laws it operates – is hardly going to change its laws for our personal belief systems. Nature seems to operate on autopilot. At times (maybe most of the time) there appear to be predetermined causes and predetermined effects. **Our wisdom lies in understanding these causes and effects and using them to our advantage.**

The Principle of Responsibility for Self

We live in an age and time in which, when things go wrong, we start looking for scapegoats. "It was someone's responsibility to do something for us correctly, and they have done it incorrectly." "Someone drove into the back of my car and I am going to sue him." "Some council or corporation officers have not allotted a flat to me when I needed it badly so I can blame my misfortune on them."

More recently a trend seems to have developed in the Western world with regard to blaming one's genes for one's problems, from alcoholism to psychopathic personality disorders. Recently there have been reports appearing in some newspapers that in the United States a convicted murderer is blaming his genes that he has inherited from his mother or father. This person says that the murders that he committed were done in a

FOOD FOR THOUGHT
As we de-stress ourselves, our needs and wants diminish – we become more prosperous and happier.

Diagram F: The Life Cycle

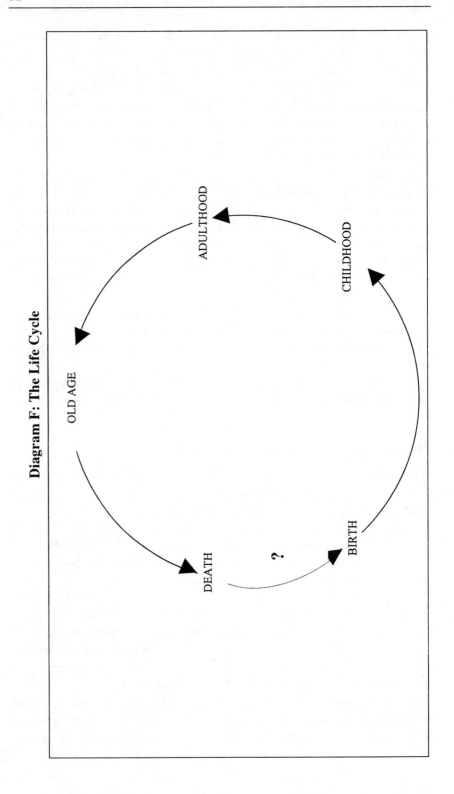

rage that resulted from the genes that he was carrying from his father. Therefore, he was not responsible for his actions.

Some of these responsibilities and blaming processes are the extreme results of our attempts to create a utopian society. This brings us to two points that have been discussed earlier. The first point is that of balances. The above examples – at least some of them – are examples of our society blaming anything and everything on everyone else and going to an extreme to do that. We seem to have lost that balance between recognising what is our responsibility and what is the responsibility of others. Another point to be considered is the principle of cause and effect. Regardless of whether we like it or believe it, Nature seems to operate on pre-set laws and principles, which if we respect can enrich our lives in many ways.

Sometimes people go through miserable experiences in life. Often, such people tend to blame Nature or sometimes God for what has befallen them. We must appreciate that for Nature, which is responsible for looking after about 6 billion people on this Earth and many star systems in the Universe, we are like small atoms. Nature is ruthless. It does not matter whether we are human being or mosquitoes. It simply continues to behave, as described before, on an autopilot basis. Our miseries might be miseries for us. From Nature's point of view, these miseries are simple effects of what we *might* have done, which is something we may or may not be aware of.

How many people can remember their birth? Hardly any. Yet we all know that we have been born. In the same way, our circumstances – happiness, unhappiness, wealth, poverty, comfort or misery – are phenomena that we bring on to ourselves. It is a different matter whether we are aware of what we have done to deserve all that. There are people in this world who do very little work and yet make a lot of money. There are also people who work from morning till night, yet they can hardly make ends meet. We can have a fatalistic outlook and say that it is because of destiny. However, another approach is to appreciate and understand that, as these people have brought onto themselves what they are doing, there is a chance that they could change what is happening to them. We are, to a certain extent, responsible for what we get. Wisdom lies in exploring the question of what is it that we do to get what we get. If we know these rules and laws – the learning of which can take a lifetime – we are richer in many ways. We become masters of our own destinies. **We can actually command Nature to do what we wish. But in order to do that we must first learn to respect Nature and its laws.**

Rule of Thumb
To change any law, we have to first follow
that law and accept that law.

The Spiritual Basis of Life

Happiness and Unhappiness

Happiness is one of the most difficult words to describe. Happiness is what we seek at every moment in our lives from the time we are born to the time we die. Happiness is as elusive as we can make it. We may seek happiness in many ways, in making money, in having sex with as many partners as possible, in gaining qualifications, in becoming political leaders, in becoming union leaders, in gaining control of everything that we do and see and in becoming athletes and players. Yet there are very few among us who can call ourselves truly happy. I have seen people who have successfully worked through therapy, who say that they have become 'happier' than before. Some of them have also described themselves as 'contented'. We have observed that as people become happier and contented they develop a glow of contentment on their faces. They become more stable in their thinking, their decision-making skills improve, they become more confident in themselves. It is fascinating that some of them also resolve their financial problems spontaneously. Interestingly, all these developments occur from within themselves. No one from outside comes to make them happy or happier. No one comes from outside to solve their problems. They do it themselves.

Happiness can be described as a state of mind. It is immaterial what kind of circumstances we are going through, what kind of bank balances we have or what kind of problems we have, we can still remain happy. Being happy does not mean that we are avoiding day to day problems. It is simply a state of mind that helps us cope better with life on a day to day basis. Some of the richest people in the world are unhappy. Why is this? Probably they have looked for happiness outside themselves. Many people who attend therapy have lots of money and power. Yet they find very little happiness in that. The moment they start working with themselves; they start finding their happiness within themselves. **Another interesting thing happens when wealthy people become happy – they attach less significance to their wealth.**

> **FOOD FOR THOUGHT**
> Whatever we have in abundance ourselves, we spontaneously give to others. It could be misery or love.

Their needs decrease – physically and materially. They become more contented within themselves.

On the other hand, we generate unhappiness within our own selves. Granted, life has its ups and downs, and there are problems that we have to sort out on a day to day basis. There are unhappy moments in life when we go through normal and abnormal losses, but, as we have discussed before, all of these situations change. **There is movement at each and every step, at every point in time in our lives. Acknowledging and accepting this movement and change and adapting to it as quickly as we can is what brings happiness.** The inability to deal with day to day difficulties and the inability to accept things as they happen in our lives ultimately leads to unhappiness. Once we start accepting whatever happens in our lives, we can pass through the event or events more quickly. This enables us to adapt to life here and now, thus clearing the way for happiness. We can remain unhappy under the same circumstances, and we can remain happy in the same circumstances. What we need are the skills to adapt quickly to change.

> *A lady was put on antidepressants for four years of her life. About six years ago she had lost her son, who was a teenager at the time. This boy had committed suicide. This lady had five other children. Working with her for a few months, it appeared that she was unprepared to move on. Despite all efforts she refused to learn newer skills to adapt. She refused to bid goodbye to her dead son.*

Another person who had gone through a loss of a similar nature came through the event and out of his unhappiness very quickly.

> *An 18-year-old man who was referred by his general practitioner with complaints about inability to focus on his work, difficulty sleeping, loss of energy for three years. His history suggested that he was grieving over his father's death, which had occurred three years before. Although he was unaware of it, this lad had lost his happiness in life as a result of the untimely death of his father. It took us just one session to clear up the baggage. As he became more accepting of his father's death, he became happier, his concentration improved and he started enjoying his life. He continues to lead a normal life.*

Holism or Wholism

We live in a world where we learn things on a piecemeal basis. This means that if we were to study geography, we would confine our learning processes to geography alone and learn about the mountains, rivers, populations and climates of various countries. When we study the history of a place, we study about who ruled whom, when, where and how. Who did what in history at a particular moment in a particular country? Which wars were fought when, and so on? In sociology we learn about how people socially interact with each other. Now looking at these three different subjects we can learn them individually – which we do most of the time. A person who has a Ph.D. in geography will know anything and everything about geography. A person who does a Ph.D. in the history of a particular country will be supposed to know a lot about the history of that country. A sociologist will know quite a bit about the sociology or the social outlook of a particular society, or societies at large. If these people were to come together and pool their knowledge about geography, history and sociology, they would understand many things about mankind more easily. Alone, their knowledge is limited. When pooled together however, their perspectives change.

They would be able to understand the reasons for Hitler's actions before the Second World War and during it. Why did he fight his battles at particular battle points and what would have happened if the climatic conditions had been different? They would also understand why Napoleon Bonaparte invaded Russia during winter and why he could not wait until summer. What geographical barriers did he have to cross and what climatic conditions did he have to face, and how did he face them? Furthermore, they would understand the outlook of Napoleon's soldiers and about the attitudes of his generals towards him and towards their subordinates.

There is a small part of the picture. There is also the bigger picture. Life is bigger than the problems that we have in it. The universe tends to operate on the basis of wholeness and holism. The bigger the picture we have, the smaller our problems are. **The more holistic our approach to life, the happier we are. Happiness is due to our ability to see the bigger picture.** Though we might study or look at things in isolation, these things affect many areas of our lives. If we are physically ill, it affects our mind, our movement, our work life, our social life, and our family life. **When we treat a physical illness, we treat all other aspects of our lives as well without necessarily being aware of it.** What problem do we have then in appreciating that many aspects of our lives are interconnected? There are many psychosomatic illnesses, that become worse with stress, and they become better when the person is relaxed. We all know that depressive illnesses occur transiently during physically strenuous periods of our lives. Psychosomatic illnesses are caused by mental stress. Physical illness creates mental stress. Each of them affect many areas of our lives.

When we are stressed out or angry, for example, our bodies respond to our emotional states. There is a resulting elevation of blood sugar, blood cholesterol and cortisol when we are stressed out.

Rule of Thumb
We can afford to be under stress for some of the days
most of the time, for most of the days some of the time
but we need to do something definite when we feel stressed
most of the days, most of the time.

Connections Between a Cell and the Universe

A cell is the smallest unit of life. It is interesting that all living cells have at least a nucleus each. Each healthy cell is controlled by its nucleus. The nucleus is present within the cell but we cannot see how it controls the cell. We can experience that it controls the cell when we study the various secretions, proteins or enzymes that leave the nucleus and that come back to the nucleus. A cell without a nucleus cannot exist. In the human body, when cancer strikes, the causative organisms or agents first destroy the nuclei of the healthy cells. This creates a form of anarchy in these cells after they have lost their control element. This causes an indiscriminate multiplication of cells causing subsequent tumour formation. **The nucleus controls the activities of the cell in unseen ways. Yet it is able to control all the activities of the cell.**

In the human body we are aware that the nervous system controls the activities of all of the organs. The nerve cells may be present in each and every cell of the body. Yet the nervous system, in unseen ways, co-ordinates with the endocrine system, and controls each and every activity of our body. When the nervous system dies, the body dies.

Every country in the world has a capital. The capital is the headquarters of the government, which usually controls the activities in that country. The government, in unseen ways, is aware of each and every activity that is going on in the country. It makes decisions and makes changes, as and when it is necessary, in unseen ways. The capital is like the nucleus of a cell. The moment the government disintegrates; the whole country falls into chaos. In the same way as cells sometimes lose their ability to fight causative agents of cancer, a country loses its fight to defend itself and to maintain its integrity once its government collapses. Anarchy follows and the country is destroyed.

The whole universe operates in similar unseen ways. Many of us are unaware of how these activities occur. We are overawed by Nature. Yet we know that there are days and nights and months and seasons that occur naturally. They occur in a cyclical way as if there are unseen forces controlling them. These forces may be present everywhere in unseen ways. Despite the fact that we cannot see it, we acknowledge that there is some kind of order in whatever happens around us in Nature. Physicists have begun to acknowledge that the different energies that they read of and study in physics seem to be divisions of the elegance of one super force with which Nature operates.

Forgiveness

One of the core characteristics of a mature person is the ability to forgive others. Forgiveness is often a misused term. When someone wrongs us, we are taught by our elders to forgive that person. But forgiveness can either be given genuinely or it can be given non-genuinely.

If we feel threatened or harmed by something or someone, one of the first emotions that are aroused is anger or fear. Depending on what our previous experiences have been, our minds tend to let our bodies do what is best for our survival – fight or flee. If we have the mentality to fight and deal with all issues that confront us or harm us, we will tend to fight. In order to fight we need energy. This energy is provided by the emotion of anger. As long as we hold on to this anger, we can *simply say* to the threat or source of harm "I forgive you". Such forgiveness has hardly any significance for the person who says he or she forgives, or the person who is said to have been forgiven. In another similar situation, the threat or the source of harm is bigger than we can handle. In such cases, our hormonal system gears up the body to enable it to flee, to run away. If we are thus cornered by an opponent who is bigger or stronger than we are, we are fearful. We are taught in such situations as well that we forgive. Practically speaking, how can we forgive someone who we are afraid of?

Forgiveness can thus be given from a different position of either anger or fear. Whenever forgiveness is tinged with anger or fear, it loses its value for both the giver and the one who is giving. When Jesus Christ was going to be crucified his famous words were:

> *Forgive them Lord, for they do not know what they are doing.*

These words were spoken without fear and without anger. That is why they have such a powerful impact on us. In saying these words, Christ demonstrated his generosity and his power. **A generous person has power.** That power can be misused to destroy others or can be put to good use by creating happiness all around. Generosity is a feeling of bigness. **A generous person is bigger than others. If we feel generous towards someone then we have a mental image of ourselves being bigger than the other person.** If we are fearful, we tend to make ourselves smaller. By construing our opponents as more powerful or worth running away from, we make them mentally bigger than they are. When angry, we consider them equal, worthy of our wrath. It is only when forgiveness comes from the heart, like the above words of Christ, that it exhibits the generosity that all of us have latent in ourselves. Forgiveness is also a sign of contentment, satisfaction and happiness within one's own self. Anger and fear result in a different feeling than happiness and satisfaction.

FOOD FOR THOUGHT: 'Love begets love' is an old adage. 'Stress begets stress is' new.

The only genuine way to forgive others is by making ourselves bigger than others. We can do so by letting go of the emotions that keep us trapped in fear or anger. Genuine forgiveness is filled with love, generosity and bigness. All other forms of forgiveness are mere words that have very little substance. **To forgive is a skill that we need to learn and develop because we need it every day at every step of our life.**

PART 2
THE STRESSED STATE

3. THE PHYSIOLOGICAL BASIS OF STRESS

Feedback Mechanisms

Physiologists tell us that there are many systems in our body that work on feedback basis. Our nervous system and endocrine (hormonal) system work on this basis as well. When the nervous system is stimulated in any form, it expresses itself in the body through the secretions of various hormones. These hormones tend to affect various processes in the body. When these hormones reach a particular level in the blood stream, they start affecting the nervous system. This effect results in a dampening down of the nervous system. This dampening down causes an inhibition of the hormones that were stimulated in the first place.

Excess secretion of one hormone affects the secretion of another hormone. If, for example, hormone A affects secretion of hormone B, hormone B can affect the secretion of hormone A as well.

Diagram G: Feedback Mechanism

HORMONE A   HORMONE B

ENDOCRINE   NERVOUS SYSTEM
SYSTEM

The conversion of water into clouds and clouds into water again is another example of a feedback mechanism. Clouds are formed as a result of evaporation of water from the seas, oceans and rivers on the ground. Low temperature is required for the clouds to be converted into water in a process called condensation. Condensation occurs in Nature. More recently scientists have used chemicals, silver nitrate for example, to condense the clouds to cause rain. What we see here is a process, which can be activated in different ways. Probably there are other ways to cause condensation of clouds to cause rains by other methods that we have yet to discover.

Feedback mechanisms seem to work everywhere in Nature. We just need to look at these mechanisms around us. Once we have knowledge of these mechanisms, it makes us masters of literally everything around us. Psychologists have long argued as to what comes first – emotions or the physiological changes that accompany them. Some psychologists believe that when we are fearful, there are changes in our bodies that precede the emotion of fear, others believe that fear comes in first before our bodies experience physiological changes. Clinically, we can affect the emotion of fear through physiological changes in the body. We can also affect the physiological changes in the body by feeling fearful. This has been used successfully in doing some forms of therapy.

Feedback mechanisms work around us in various forms and ways. We need to learn the skills to be able to perceive these mechanisms at various levels. **Once we master these skills we can become adept at solving problems in our lives by doing very little.** When someone is under stress, the person can help himself or herself by using these feedback mechanisms.

The Role of the Nervous System

The nervous system is one of the various systems in our body that co-ordinates various biological activities. The nervous system is also called the controlling system of our body. We can appreciate the role of the nervous system by becoming aware that the nervous system 'controls' by 'co-ordinating' the various systems in our bodies. This is one of the biggest secrets in human physiology. Like the nervous system, which co-ordinates various systems, we can co-ordinate with Nature, to control various aspects of our lives.

Broadly speaking, the nervous system is divided into three parts:
• the central nervous system;
• the autonomic nervous system;
• the peripheral nervous system.

We need to appreciate here that even though we study these systems separately, they work in tandem with each other and are an integral part and parcel of the nervous system, which itself is only one of the systems in the body. The other systems are the digestive system, respiratory system, excretory system, circulatory system, reproductive system, skeletal system, sensory system, muscular system and endocrine system. All of these systems work together to make a whole person. The central nervous system comprises the brain, which is connected to the spinal chord. It is also connected with the autonomic nervous systems, which control the functioning of our internal organs. On the periphery, on the surface of our bodies, are peripheral nerves, which are connected with the central nervous system. The peripheral nervous system co-ordinates muscular contraction and relaxation and also makes the rest of the nervous system aware of the environment outside our bodies. Affected by the information that is perceived by the nervous system, the nervous system co-operates with other bodily systems to make changes within the body, to adjust itself to survive and to enable us to live happily. We are discussing the nervous system here in preference to other systems of the body only because it co-ordinates the other systems. All of the other systems in our bodies are equally important. **Our bodies are examples of wholes made up of many parts.**

The autonomic nervous system controls the internal organs of the body. This system – as the name implies – is automatic. Scientists have believed that this system is involuntary, i.e. we cannot voluntarily control the autonomic nervous system. The autonomic nervous system controls the rate of our heart beat, the strength at which our hearts beat, the expansion and contraction of blood vessels in the body and the juices that are secreted in the digestive system at various times. Our breathing processes, our immune system, the ability of our body to produce and pass water in the form of urine are also controlled by it. Most of these activities are controlled through enzymes and hormones secreted within our bodies. The hormonal system and the nervous system affect each other. Nervous stimulation stimulates the production or inhibition of hormones. Nervous inhibition stimulates the production and inhibition of other hormones.

When we get angry, for example, our nervous system helps in the production of certain hormones that bring about changes in our bodies to fight the source of anger.

Rule of Thumb

The more stressed we are, the more angry, fearful and insecure we become. Anger, fear and insecurity increase our stress in turn.

Diagram H: Representation Diagram Showing
Connections in the Nervous System

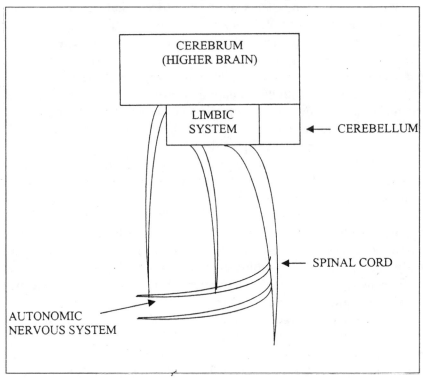

The autonomic nervous system itself can be studied under two headings:

1. Sympathetic nervous system.
2. Parasympathetic nervous system.

The sympathetic and parasympathetic nervous systems control or co-ordinate with each other by balancing against each other. When the sympathetic system is aroused, the parasympathetic system balances it. When the parasympathetic system is aroused causing inhibition, the sympathetic system opposes that and stimulates whatever the parasympathetic system inhibits. The sympathetic nervous system, as the name implies, is sympathetic to the survival of our bodies. 'Para' means 'around'. The sympathetic nervous system is usually stimulating. It controls a variety of physiological functions: increased heartbeat, constriction of blood vessels, availability of sugars in the bloodstream, availability of stress hormones such as cortisol, increased breathing rate, dilation of pupils, sweating, contraction of muscles, decreased

Diagram I: Feedback Mechanism in Autonomic Nervous System

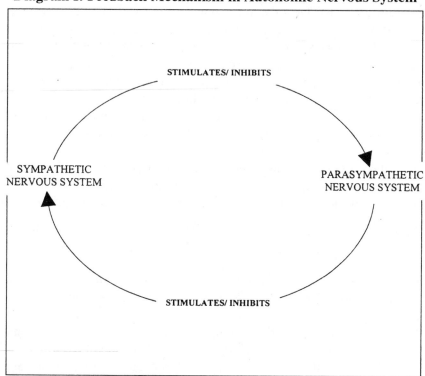

amount of digestive enzymes, decreased movement of muscles of the digestive tract and inhibition of defecation and urination. The parasympathetic nervous system has exactly the opposite effect; for example, it decreases the heart rate, expands the blood vessels, increases digestive enzymes and promotes defecation and urination besides other activities. In order to achieve balance, the two systems have to oppose, co-ordinate and control each other.

If the sympathetic system is stimulated to the extent that the parasympathetic system has no control over it, then the body burns itself out and dies. On the other hand, stimulating the parasympathetic system to its extreme so that the sympathetic system loses control can also cause death. It is through the stimulation of the parasympathetic system that mystics are sometimes said to go into a state of voluntary death.

Theoretically, the autonomic nervous system cannot be controlled voluntarily. However, if we look at the various principles that we have learned earlier, the sympathetic and the parasympathetic system can be balanced and controlled comparatively easily. Moreover, we can use this balance to co-ordinate the other systems of the body and align them in such a way as to create happiness for ourselves. Working on the feed-back hypothesis, mystics over the ages have been controlling their breathing, which affects the autonomic nervous system and helps them to control their heartbeats, blood pressure and every other system in their bodies. Once we become aware of these phenomena and how they operate, we can control all of the aspects of our lives. We can diminish our stress or we can increase our stress whenever there is a need. We can use the stress that we generate to our advantage.

The respiratory system is not the only internal system that has been used to control our internal environment. Our sensory system and other systems have been used as well with equal benefit. We can use the sense of sight by seeing, or even imagining seeing, beautiful places. It affects our nervous system, which in turn affects the control of the internal organs of our body. Such methods of therapy have been widely used in hypnosis.

The Role of Neurotransmitters

Neurotransmitters are chemicals that exist in our nervous system. These chemicals help our nervous system to operate smoothly. Neurotransmitters are directly under the influence of the nervous system. However, they can be indirectly affected by external factors. Any emotional arousal or inhibition can stimulate or retard production of a neurotransmitter. Noradrenaline, adrenaline, acetylcholine, dopamine, glycine and serotonin are some of the neurotransmitters that are widely known. As explained before, neurotransmitters tend to decrease or increase in concentration in our nervous system, depending on various factors that affect us.

It has been found that when a person is happy, the production of dopamine is increased. Certain cells present in the brain also secrete acetylcholine, usually secreted by the parasympathetic system. This neurotransmitter has been said to cause depression. On the other hand, an increase in the neurotransmitter noradrenaline causes excitation. Increased sensitivity of certain receptors in the brain causes an illness called schizophrenia. A lack of or a decrease in the secretion of serotonin in the brain is said to cause aggressive behaviour in people. It also causes difficulties in sleep.

> *A young man went to see a psychiatrist for feelings of sadness with decreased concentration, energy and ability to enjoy day to day life. The psychiatrist told him that he was suffering from a biochemical imbalance in the brain for which he needed medication. He was advised that medica-*

*tion was the only form of treatment that was available with
which he could benefit.*

This is the usual story with people who go to seek medical help for their
mental illnesses. Most of the time Nature is shown as a necessary devil
that is trying to get at us in the form of such illnesses. Little do we realise that if Nature has given us these illnesses, there must be ways to
work with Nature to deal with such conditions. Medical advice such as
was given to the young man in the story above is taken very seriously
indeed and the suffering person believes rightly or wrongly that his or
her world starts and ends with medication from then on. Millions of
people around the world have the very same impression about mental
illnesses and medication.

Neurotransmitters are said to play a role in causation of mental illnesses. This occurs when they affect us too little or too much and there
is an imbalance in their proportion to each other. This proportionality
has yet to be understood properly by psychiatrists. Once again, mental
illnesses seem to be caused by an imbalance between the stimulatory
and inhibitory neurotransmitters in our nervous system. This imbalance
between the two systems occurs whenever our bodies and our minds
undergo stress. By developing our abilities to recognise stress and
quickly deal with the situation or the event causing it or by changing
ourselves to accommodate to the new situation, we can reverse such
imbalances.

The Role of Emotions

The way we are conceived and the way we all die are emotional experiences. In the period between conception and death most of our intimate
experiences are also emotional in nature. **Human beings are emotional
animals.** Stones cannot cry, or scream, or be angry, or be sad. We can.
**Emotions are gifts from Nature to us that help us deal with moment
to moment living.** Emotions can also cause difficulties for a person if
expressed inappropriately to an extreme.

Emotions have a use in our lives that we in developed societies have
gone to extremes to curtail. Once again, we seem to have lost our balance in deciding what are appropriate and what are inappropriate
expressions of emotions. In order to create more productivity, because
our survival was at stake, the progressive industrial civilisation discour-
aged people from expressing their emotions. This was probably because
it was thought that such expressions would hinder growth in the material world. If a person spent time grieving or feeling sad, or feeling
angry, it was a waste of time. This time could be very efficiently used to

create some more material wealth. So some of the commonest phrases in the industrialised world are 'get on with life', 'stop crying', 'stop being a child' or 'be a grown up, it is not the time to be emotional'. As a consequence, **we never seem to have time to be emotional. Maybe it would have been helpful if we did.**

During the last two centuries or so a lot of progress has probably been made by cognitive efforts of man. Cognitive – because man has spent the last two centuries at least thinking about possibilities of making more money and creating more wealth. The emotional part that throws up ideas into the cognitive brain has been ignored to a great extent. Only during the last few years have we started waking up to the emotional part of our brain. Daniel Goleman's book *Emotional Intelligence* was one of the first works in this area. Emotions were suddenly recognised to be quite important in a person's life. Knowledge and experience with the emotional aspects of the brain, though slow, have made us more aware of the potential of paying attention to this area.

Emotions seem to be the most powerful forces that drive mankind. Emotions have created histories, destroyed families, made commoners out of kings (Duke of Windsor) and made dictators out of commoners (Fidel Castro, Mao Zedong, Oliver Cromwell). Emotions are the most powerful forces that motivate us to act and behave.

When buying a car, we might decide on the brand of car and the type of car that we want to buy, depending on how much we are prepared to pay. At the end of it all, the colour of the car we buy depends on our likes and dislikes. Liking and disliking something or someone is a spontaneous experience. However emotional or cognitive we might be, at the end of the day the colour of the car that we choose depends on our emotional state at that particular moment in time. Our favourite colour is also determined by our usual mood state. If we look at the process of choosing colour for a car, cognition hardly comes into play. Emotions are sometimes said to be more intense versions of feelings. The way we feel comfortable with some people and uncomfortable with others has hardly anything to do with our higher intelligence. It is what we call *lower* intelligence, which drives us and determines with whom we like to interact and with whom we do not like to interact.

Knowledge about how emotions affect our lives is the key to knowing how to use them to our advantage. One of the fundamental problems that we have been having with emotions over the last two centuries has been the advice that parents have been giving to their children, which promotes the suppression of emotions. This suppression creates stress, which if it becomes chronic, leads on to mental illness.

Defining Stress

Various people have defined stress in various ways. Stress has been described as 'good stress' (eustress) and 'bad stress' (stress). It can be a little confusing to use the same term for something 'good' and 'bad'. Is there a difference between good stealing and bad stealing? When stealing is done for a good cause is it good stealing and if it is done for a bad cause is it bad stealing. **Although it could be a matter of semantics, words have very strong influence on our non-cognitive mind.** In the present day world, the word 'stress' is enough to cause stress in any mind that would be calm enough to read or listen to this word.

What is Stress?

Our muscles and our nerves are in a constant state of tension. This tension in scientific terms is called 'tonus'. The tonus in a muscle is present when the muscle is alive. The tonus is that quality of a muscle that makes it contract. A freshly cut muscle with its connected nerve will tend to contract when placed on a flat surface. This contraction is caused by the tension in the muscle. **Relaxation is an active process of the muscle, and it is not necessarily spontaneous. Tension in the body is a sign of life.** It is this tension which is called eustress or good stress. When the tension in the body increases beyond an arbitrary limit, it becomes bad stress. It is this stress that is called stress in layman's terms. It is this stress that we tend to cope with using various mechanisms. It is this stress that we need the skills to deal with on a day to day basis in order to improve the quality of our lives.

In the early part of the 20th century, Hans Selye, a Canadian endocrinologist, postulated a theory that our bodies undergo what he called a General Adaptation Syndrome during stress. This syndrome has three stages:
* alarm reaction;
* resistance;
* exhaustion.

These three stages illustrate how our bodies respond to stress.

During the first stage – alarm reaction – our bodies become tense, our pulse rate increases. Our minds may start to wander as we lose our concentration. We are unable to relax. As we continue the activity that is putting us under stress, we reach the stage of resistance.

During the resistance stage, we tend to fight the stress by overcoming it with various activities. Among the most common activities that we use in this stage are smoking, drinking tea or coffee and drinking alcohol. After consuming one of these stimulants (alcohol is a stimulant in low doses), we initially become more active than before. We get a false feeling of stress having been overcome.

The stage of exhaustion occurs when we become physically and mentally exhausted. Once we reach this stage, we enter the danger areas of physical and mental illness. At such moments we have to choose either to stop completely or to continue doing our activity. By choosing to continue, we make it certain that we will suffer both physically and mentally.

Stress is a gift that nature has given to us to deal with threatening situations. Imagine living 700 years ago, when life was lived without the help of any machines. Life was very slow. People worked in agriculture or were manual workers. Their needs were few; their life was simple. Telephone, car, television, radio, aeroplane, electricity and computers were unheard of. Life was simple. Needs were few. Stresses in life occurred only when there was an attack from an enemy. Wild animals, illnesses and natural calamities were other stressors.

There was far less sensory stimulation than there is at the present time. It was only during a time of threat that stress entered life.

Advances in communication, transport and education mean that today there are many stimulations in our environment and our nervous system perceives these stimulations as threats to internal peace. When this internal peace is disturbed, our nervous system perceives it as a threat. This perceived threat is what we call stress. Our bodies and our minds work together. So our bodies and our minds together gear us up to deal with perceived threats. This puts our bodies and our minds in positions of fight or flight, causing stress.

Seven hundred years ago when human beings faced illnesses, natural catastrophes, animals and enemies successfully, there was a phase of peace and quietness that could continue for a long time. Our present lifestyles, with seemingly endless activities and work, social and family responsibilities prevent us from being at peace with our own selves. This is especially true in urban areas, with struggles to reach the workplace in time and exposure to the noises of the city. All of these factors lead to stress.

Neurotransmitters and Stress

As explained before, noradrenaline and adrenaline are hormones that are circulated in our circulatory system ensuring that we continue to live. During stressful situations, another hormone called cortisol is secreted. The presence of this hormone in blood creates more glucose concentration, high levels of cholesterol and increased low-density lipoproteins. If this situation is temporary, the body can recover quickly from stress. Ongoing day to day city life with all of its stimulations creates a chronic condition of stress that is perpetuated by over-activity and a lack of relaxation. Most of the premature deaths that occur in young people, leading even so called healthy lifestyles, but devoid of relaxation, are due to similar conditions. When we are de-stressed the optimal amount of glucose, amino acids, cholesterol and lipoproteins that is necessary for our bare survival is circulating in our blood. In such a condition, the body and mind are usually happy and contented.

Physical and Mental Stress

Body and mind work together. The way our bodies operate and behave depends on how our mind responds to life's situations. How our minds think is also affected by our physical condition. Post-natal depression and depression following surgery are conditions that are well known to doctors. In these conditions, theoretically speaking, it is the body that undergoes some form of vigorous activity or change. All of the body's energies have to focus on the primary activity at hand, whether it is childbirth or letting the body deal with the loss of a diseased part. If our bodies and our minds were working separately, why should someone suffer depression following childbirth or a surgical operation on the body?

FOOD FOR THOUGHT
We create stress by running our lives as businesses.

People who have been victims of earthquakes and natural catastrophes have been known to develop skin diseases, especially psoriasis. These diseases can appear within two or three days of an earthquake. In some instances, people have developed eczema, as a result of undergoing a lot of mental stress. We have seen cases in psychiatry where a person has lost the proper use of a limb or limbs following a traumatic event. Such conditions are known as conversion disorders. If the mind and the body were entirely independent of each other, it would be impossible for a sensory or a motor conversion disorder to be caused by a traumatic event. Our current system of learning, which treats subjects as separate topics totally unrelated to any other subject, has made our thinking longitudinal or linear. When medical students are taught anatomy, physiology, biochemistry and medicine as separate subjects in medical schools, many tend to forget that all of these systems pertain to one human body, which also comprises the brain. At any given moment as long as we live, all our systems, including our nervous system, work in tandem with one another. This way of linear learning encourages us to ignore the holistic pattern of life.

The origin of stress can be physical or mental or both. Our mind perceives threats to our body or our mind as threats affecting the whole individual. In reality, a threat to life may or may not exist. If we scratch any part of our skin with a sharp object, a message is immediately conveyed to our nervous system. This creates a response, which we see as inflammation on the skin. All of the instructions of the brain to our skin are to respond to this particular touch in a way so that whatever damage has been done to the tissues can be reversed and repaired. This is one way in which our brain or our nervous system responds to a physical threat.

When one's nervous system anticipates a threat, it conveys messages to various systems of one's body to prepare to deal with this threat. Even though the threat may be totally absent, it is the perception of the situation being threatening that makes our mind behave in such a way as to make the body ready to deal with the threat when it occurs. This is a situation of stress.

Stress as a perceived threat can be physical or mental, but whatever the case, it affects our bodies and our minds together. People have been known to suffer from high blood pressure at a young age without any specific physical cause. Such people have a tendency to experience stress most of the time. When we are physically tired, our mind also would like to let our body be rested. In such situations we find we get irritable if there is too much stimulation around us. Therefore, when we are physically tired, exhausted or stressed, our mind is also under stress. When we are worried, anxious and anticipating a stimulating situation, our mind becomes very active. This results in mental stress. It affects our bodies by an increase in heart rate, constriction or narrowing of blood vessels, sometimes causing sweating and clamminess in the skin. It also brings about other physical changes affecting the digestive system, the urinary system, the respiratory system and other systems. Stress, whether it is physical or mental, affects both our minds and our bodies at the same time. Stress also affects our thinking, our behaviours, and our perception of events and situations. It is for this reason that stress has to be looked at in its wholeness rather than in isolation. How stress affects these aspects is discussed elsewhere.

Stressors

Stressors are agents that cause stress. Stressors can be divided into two broad categories:
- external;
- internal.

Diagram J: Our Nervous System Responds to Real and Perceived Threats in the Same Way

Response to Perceived Threat

DEFENSIVE RESPONSE (STRESS)

INCREASED AROUSAL

MESSAGE TO BRAIN

PERCEIVED THREAT

OVERSTIMULATION OF SENSES

Response to Real Threat

DEFENSIVE RESPONSE (FIGHT/FLIGHT)

INCREASED AROUSAL

MESSAGE TO BRAIN

PHYSICAL HURT

PHYSICAL THREAT

External Stressors

External stressors are the sources of stress that we are aware of around us. These stressors are things that create a situation of perceived threat in our minds and bodies. Over the last few years a lot of research has been done on external stressors. These stressors can affect us in various settings – at work, at home, while driving and in a social setting. As discussed earlier, we are all free spirits in Nature. Anything that constrains our freedom of expression, thought or action creates a situation of stress that our bodies and our minds would like to change. It results in a feeling of unhappiness and discontent. For example, the same home can be a happy place or a stressful place. If things do not happen according to our desires at home, our wishes are unfulfilled and we feel stressed.

In the workplace, our expectations of our work, our employers, our colleagues and our own commitments, if unfulfilled, create a situation that our mind perceives as threat. We find ourselves helpless and unable to change the situation. Our free spirit is stilted. We feel the 'pressure'. This is stress.

While commuting to work or home, or in our social lives, our desire to be free remains unfulfilled. For example, when we are driving in the morning, traffic behaves in an undesirable way. We have to reach our office in time to keep that appointment, but the driver in front is driving slowly or rashly. We would like the road to be clear of all traffic so that we could reach our appointment within the next five minutes. Our freedom is curtailed. We are angry, sometimes frustrated. Our mind perceives the situation as a threat. The body follows the mind. This is stress.

Internal Stressors

Internal stressors are the stressors inside us. These are stressors that have been in our minds and bodies for many years of our lives. These stressors exist in the form of our genetic loading. They are also restrictions that have been imposed on us by our parents, our teachers, and various authority figures that have taught us what to do, and more importantly what not to do. Such internal stressors remain in our bodies, unknown to us, in the form of emotions. According to recent research done in the United States, such emotions exist in our bodies in the form of neurochemicals called neuropeptides. Neuropeptides are laid out in our cell systems in such a manner that the patterns are hard to delete. Such patterns, when laid out with our emotional experiences, persist

FOOD FOR THOUGHT
A wise man recognises his limitations and works within his resources.

for our lifetime. In this form, stress is stored in our bodies. These stresses or negative emotions or neuropeptides are organised in such a way as to affect our perception, our thinking and our behaviour. These stresses become chronic.

The interaction of the external stressors and the internal stresses create what we call stress. The internal stressors mentioned above, when interacting with the external stressors (environment), create arousal in our body systems. The internal stressors then become stress.

The Interaction between External and Internal Stressors

In physics we learn from magnetism that each magnet has a magnetic field in which it has influence. A simple iron piece has no magnetic properties. Therefore, we can hardly experience its magnetic influence. When two magnets of equal strength are in proximity to each other so that their magnetic fields overlap, the two forces tend to oppose each other. This opposition of forces leads to an expenditure of energy.

If a plain iron piece is brought near a magnet of an equal size, the magnet influences the iron piece and attracts the iron piece towards itself. The iron piece becomes magnetised and this magnetic property that is induced by the magnet is called induced magnetism. When the iron piece, now induced magnet, is removed from the influence of the inducing magnet, it loses its magnetic property after some time.

Stress is like the force that is experienced when two magnets come into proximity with each other. When the internal stressors and external stressors interact, there is a reaction between the two, which creates stress in our minds and bodies. If we have internal stressors only and our outer environment is placid and happy, we have little reason for disturbance inside of us and can be stress free. If there are very active external stressors in our lives but few or no emotional stressors, we will have little disturbance in our minds or bodies. We can then be stress free. When we have no internal and external stressors interacting with each other, there is happiness, calmness and creativity.

We can develop skills that will enable us to become like the simple iron piece above. When we are emotionally cleaned of negative influences, we become like the iron piece. The external environment, however stressful it might be, has very limited influence on us. The external forces of stress then have limited effects on our lives.

In psychiatry, stressors are called aetiological factors. External stressors are called social aetiological factors, and internal stressors are called psychological and genetic aetiological factors. From the current psychiatric point of view, there is hardly anything that we can do to change the effects of genetic and psychological factors in producing stress.

Diagram K: Creation of Stress

STRESS

INTERNAL STRESSORS

EXTERNAL STRESSORS

OVERLAPPING MAGNETIC FIELDS

MAGNET B

MAGNET A

Conditioning and Stress

Conditioning theories have contributed significantly to understanding the behaviour and thinking patterns of human beings and other animals. Conditioning is a process by which our mind gets tuned into thinking and behaving in a particular pattern on receiving certain cues. Cues can be anything that can be perceived by any of our senses. A sound, a voice, a particular face, a particular situation, a specific smell or a particular way a person is touched can produce predictable responses. When responses become predictable, the pattern can be changed in order to affect the behaviour and thinking of a person.

There are two types of conditioning:

* classical;
* operant.

In classical conditioning, discovered by Pavlov, a stimulus that is repeated many times produces a predictable response called a conditioned response. In operant conditioning, a reinforcer is used to produce the response. In order to consolidate the response behaviour, an incentive is given after each response. This increases the frequency of the predictable response following a particular cue or stimulus.

Although conditioning processes have been studied and used in changing the thinking and behaviour of people, they have wider applications. Fascinatingly, it has been seen clinically that our minds are conditioned to arouse certain kinds of emotions within us that affect our various systems and produce physiological responses. If a person has been feeling angry during the early years of his or her life, listening to the verbal assaults of a parent, then the experiences condition the person's bodily systems to respond in a particular way. Later in life, when such a person hears a tone of voice that resembles the parental voice, the same emotions are aroused again and these emotions affect the thinking and behaviour of the person.

Meeting deadlines and targets for higher performance and more productivity are daily occurrences that are stimulating to our minds. This stimulation tends to create a state of arousal within our bodies and our minds. This state of arousal can become positive and propel us to achieve higher goals. However, if such stimulation arouses negative emotions within us, it can harm us in many ways. Perception of stress is thus a conditioned response to whatever stimuli stress us.

> **FOOD FOR THOUGHT**
> **Productivity needs hard physical work. Creativity needs none.**

Diagram L:

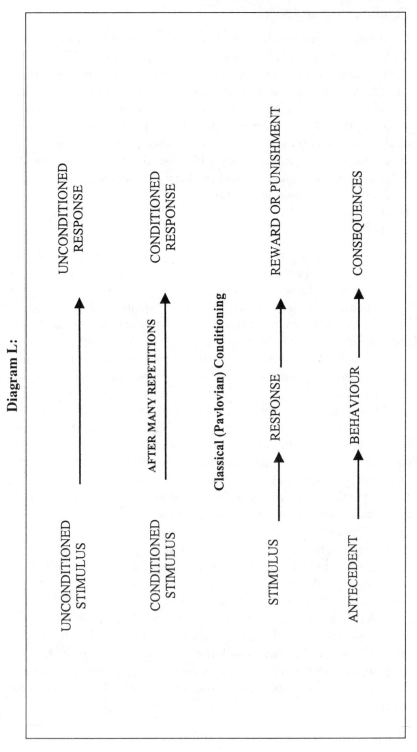

Theory of Relativity and Stress

Most of the happenings in nature are relative. If night is dark, it is darker with respect to day. If the day is bright, then it is brighter as compared to night. During dusk, it is brighter than night but darker than day.

The absolute happenings in nature are extreme happenings. Life and death are two extremes of a continuum. Something is living because it is relative to something that is dead. This relativity also applies to stress. If someone, suppose we call this person A, is stressed-out, then this person is under more stress than someone who is relaxed. However, A still may be under less stress than someone whose life is being threatened by a gun to their head. So A may be comparatively more relaxed than the person who has a gun to their head. Similarly a de-stressed person, or a relaxed person, may still be more active or more stressed out compared to someone who is playing dead.

The point at which we start to feel stressed or de-stressed changes from one person to the other. Feelings of stress or de-stress are not quantifiable. They are arbitrary in nature and can change from time to time, place to place and person to person. Two people under similar circumstances would respond and be affected by the same circumstances quite differently. For one, the situation could be stressful, for the other, the situation could be less stressful or more relaxed. Say for example, if Mr A and Mr B are climbing a mountain. Mr B is an experienced mountaineer. Mr A is comparatively inexperienced. If Mr B is older and Mr A is younger, then the stress which Mr A will bear will be more than the stress that Mr B will experience. Mr B could be more relaxed climbing the mountain as compared to Mr A. Mr B would feel less stress as compared to Mr A. This arbitrariness in the perceptions of stress and de-stress is important in order to appreciate the terms.

The Mind-Body Connection in Stress

During the early part of the 20th century, Freud hypothesised that there were certain parts of our brain that were active in such a way, that with our senses active at all times we were oblivious to the activity of these parts of the brain. He called these parts together the Unconscious. The Unconscious, as he described it, was responsible for looking after the survival of the individual. In order to help the individual to survive, the Unconscious would usually change the perception, the thinking and the behaviour of a person.

A young woman came into the clinic walking on crutches.
All of the investigations carried out in the hospital sug-

gested that she was perfectly healthy. She had an accom-
panying lower backache. Her complaints had developed
over the previous year. She had stopped attending work
many months before she stopped walking. Her absence
from work, now due to her inability to walk, was triggered
by an armed robbery at her workplace in which she was
also a victim.

This young woman had unconsciously, to assure her survival, physically refused to go to work. From her conscious perspective, she was
willing to go back to work whenever she became well. This was an
example of someone who had become so emotionally aroused during
the robbery, that without finding an emotional release, she had led herself to believe that she could not go to work. It was a classical example
of emotional pressure affecting perception, thinking and behaviour.

Wilhelm Reich, an Austrian-born psychotherapist, has described
what he calls body armour. According to him our body acts as an
armour to prevent ourselves from expressions of emotion that we find
unsociable to express. This was hardly the first time that the mind-body
connection had been mentioned in psychology literature. **Our bodies
when under stress affect our minds. Our minds, when under stress,
make our bodies tense. If the body relaxes, it helps the mind relax.
When the mind relaxes, it eases the tension in the body.**

Stress is perceived threat. When our bodies or minds perceive anything that threatens our existence, we feel stress. One of the components
of stress is physical tension. This tension is caused by the contraction of
the body's muscles.

Whenever we are threatened, we spontaneously tend to
become small in size. A child, when frightened, would
cover his or her head as the first instinctual response. A
frightened person, being physically or mentally threat-
ened, would tend to make their body as small as possible.

We spontaneously tend to become smaller physically when our lives are
threatened. This usually happens after an attempt to flee or fight has
failed. To make the body smaller our muscles need to contract. Interestingly, our minds seem to contract as well. An individual in danger,
would have a fixed gaze, would focus their thoughts on escape, and
would make the body ready to fight or flee. If fighting or fleeing, we
cuddle up to make our body like a ball. It is as if we make an invisible
shell around our exterior when it is exposed to threat. A porcupine when
in danger would do the same. It makes itself into a ball with its spikes
on the outside towards the enemy. Such posture also closes us to any

exposure to the environment. Interestingly our mind also becomes focused on survival and closes itself to all environmental experiences during stress.

In other words, when we are threatened, our body and mind work together in tandem as components of a single system. At such moments of threat, survival of the individual is the most important activity for the individual. If a person were to have difficulty in channelling all of their energies and resources to deal with the threat, the threat could trample the individual. This could lead to the death of the individual. When either our bodies or our minds conclude that we are under any threat, this information is exchanged with the other component of the system. This also means that when either mind or body perceives a relaxed situation, this information is also relayed to the other component in the system spontaneously. When the body experiences stress or de-stress the mind spontaneously learns about it and accepts it. When the mind perceives any stress or de-stress, it conveys the message to the body and the body accepts it. This one fact explains, as well as raises, many questions about therapies in general.

Rule of Thumb
To deal with stress, we need to act on it *before* it
hits us rather than *when* it hits us.

---

4. THE EFFECTS OF STRESS

Perception, Thinking, Behaviour, Emotion

Our behaviours are external manifestations of our perceptions, thoughts and emotions. Our perceptions are the interpretations we make when we sense anything through our senses. Our thoughts can affect our perceptions. Our perceptions can also affect our thoughts. Emotions are internal processes that, when aroused, can affect our thinking processes. Our thoughts can also affect our emotions. The connection among these four components can be presented as follows.

**Diagram M: Relationship of Perception,
Thinking, Behaviour and Emotions**

PERCEPTION

EMOTIONS   AFFECTS   THINKING

BEHAVIOUR

This connection has been used over the last few decades to help people change their lives through various forms of therapy.

> *When I arrived in Dublin many years ago, I had the oppor-*
> *tunity to go to a local hospital office, with a friend, who is*

also a doctor. This friend is also from India. As we were going up the stairs to the office, we met a local lady, who informed us that the office was closed. This lady, who was a stranger to us, addressed us as doctors. After we asked what made her think we were doctors, the lady replied "all Indians are doctors".

This is a classic example of the interaction of the four components, which is described above. The lady perceived us as doctors and thought of us respectfully with positive emotions. Her behaviour towards us was very friendly.

Diagram N: The System of Relaxation

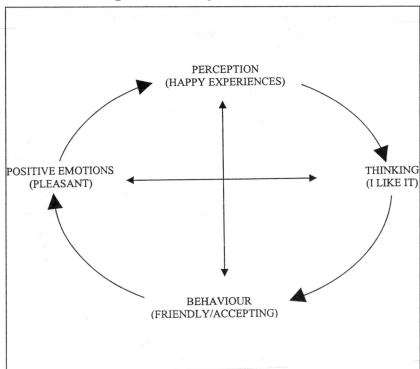

In negative situations all four components – perception, thought, emotions and behaviour – become negative. This causes stress. Threat is perceived in this way. Changing even one component among the four components alters the whole pattern of response. Perception and thinking can be changed by direct or indirect suggestions. Change in one of them can bring about changes in the other three components of the system. This phenomenon can be used to produce or decrease stress.

Diagram O: The System of Stress

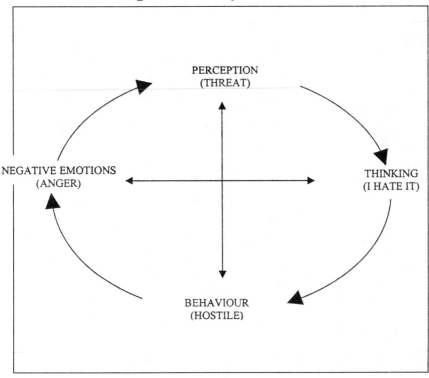

A lady was referred with complaints of feeling depressed, having nightmares and flashbacks and being fearful of travelling in trains ever since she was involved in a train accident. She was treated successfully using desensitisation techniques. She was later able to travel successfully, and without any fear, on trains.

In this example, the emotion of fear is linked with the perception of a train journey being fearful. The thought of a train journey would also bring up emotions of fear. The behaviour of this lady when thinking of a train was to run away from it and to avoid it completely. She was in a state of stress – a state of perceived threat. A change in *any* one of the components in the system of perception, emotion, thought and behaviour would have brought changes in her attitudes towards the train journey.

Emotions and Stress

Human beings are emotional animals. From the time we are born to the time we die, we have to experience emotions in one form or another. Modern day education has encouraged people to become more and more educated and less and less emotional. Our peers, our teachers, our elders teach us, to get along in life. Whenever there is a loss or bereavement, a shock, a sad experience or a threatening experience, we are repeatedly told to 'forget it' and to carry on with life.

In attempts to forget things, we continue to remember them until these emotions have fully lived their cycle and died. Emotions tend to affect all aspects of our lives. Emotions give us energy. They act as forces that propel us in the various activities in our life.

> *A young man came in to seek help for a poor relationship with his girlfriend. On exploring the issues that were problematic for him, he learnt that he had a lot of anger towards his parents. On suggesting that it would be helpful for him to let go of this anger, to get along with life more positively and more constructively, he resisted. His plea was that it was anger that had pushed him to make a lot of money and succeed in life in that direction. If he would lose that anger, it would affect his material progress. Therefore, he found it difficult to give his anger up.*

Freud's work in exploring neurosis is pertinent to this discussion. In simple terms, our suppressed emotions affect our behaviour in many ways. These suppressed emotions can cause anxiety.

In simpler terms, negative emotions such as anger and fear, when suppressed within our nervous system, are like steam suppressed in a pressure cooker. In the same way as steam builds up against the walls of the pressure cooker in its attempts to escape, our emotions tend to seek outlets of release from our nervous system. And, as with the pressure cooker, when the steam is eventually able to get out of the valve, it is released with a lot of pressure. It has a lot of energy in the form of heat and this energy can burn human skin. Similarly, the release of emotions in human beings is seen in behaviours. When these emotions are released, with force, the energy created affects many lives. Unfortunately, this release of emotions is usually destructive.

In a stressful situation, when threat is perceived, we tend to be emotionally aroused. This emotional arousal is suppressed by the social system around us. We are unable to express ourselves. **This bottled up stress starts controlling our thinking and our behaviours.**

In order to alleviate this stress, we resort to various means of behaviour. We may start to drink, abuse drugs or engage in excessive physical exercise or any other activity that we feel will lower our stress levels. The more stressed we are, the more we indulge in these activities and behaviours. If there is a limit placed on our behaviours, our emotions will find their outlet in our thinking patterns. We start thinking excessively in a particular way or direction. We may become focused and blinkered. When under stress, any neutral stimulus that we observe or come in contact with has a threatening meaning for us because of our altered perception.

Stress and Personality

Emotions seem to act like the mortar that is used in the building of our personalities. If this mortar is of good quality and is positive, the building will be beautiful, long lasting and attractive to the people around. If the emotions are negative then the mortar is of poor quality; the building of our personality will be weak and will crumble. It will lose its attraction for anybody around.

Personality is the sum total of our physical, mental, behavioural and emotional attributes. Some kinds of personalities are said to be stressed out personalities. In particular, Type A personality behaviour comes to mind. People with Type A personality are always on the go, find it difficult to sit still, sit on the edge of their chairs, rush round, and are constantly engaged in activity. Emotions play a significant part in creating stress and in the type of de-stressing activities that we resort to.

Our emotional experiences, after we are born, stay with us for the rest of our lives. This is true until we actively work out our emotions to cleanse ourselves of them. Current parenting skills and the education system fall far short of such expectations. Our emotions stay with us for our whole lives. Recent research by Candace Pert and her colleagues has demonstrated that our emotions stay with us in the form of neuropeptide linkages. These neuropeptides are present in each and every part of our body. They are changed by emotions. Once constructed, they stay with us in the form of emotional memories. These neuropeptides enable us to think and behave in stereotyped ways as a result of our emotional experiences.

Research in child development carried out by Bowlby, a psychologist who was prominent

FOOD FOR THOUGHT
Stress is like wealth – the more we generate, the more we can give to others. We can, of course, hoard it for our own use and the use of our next generation.

in the late – 1950s and 1960s, is very significant with regard to the development of personalities. Bowlby concluded that a child reared in a very secure environment grows up to be a confident and secure adult. This positive adult contributes positively to life. This secure adult's perception and thinking are positive. This adult can also let things go and still feel secure. This person is self-sufficient to a great extent. **Recent research in child psychology has confirmed that children brought up in uncaring or hostile environments tend to become insecure adults. Such people usually lack the ability to exploit their own potential.**

Higher Brain and Lower Brain

The characteristic feature of human development is what is called cephalisation. Anthropologists have described it as the enlargement of the cerebral hemispheres of the human nervous system. Cerebral hemispheres are anatomically parts of the higher brain. The cerebral hemispheres are actively involved in learning facts and absorbing knowledge through experiences from the environment and, to a certain extent, they affect our capacity to make decisions.

The lower brain is the emotional part of the brain, which lies below the cerebral hemispheres. The limbic system and so-called archicerebellum (the old brain) is what is called the lower brain. This part of the brain helps us to appreciate and express emotions. The higher brain helps us to reason, use logic, and learn facts. The lower brain is hardly concerned with any fact or reason. It is the instinctual, impulsive part of the brain. This is the part of the brain that plays a role in crying, feeling angry, and liking or disliking something or someone. As mentioned before, however logical we might be, it is the lower brain that decides our likes or dislikes and determines how we behave. Our logic is backed by our likes and dislikes. For example, the logical decision of buying a car of a particular colour depends on our liking for that colour. This comes from our lower brain. As our likes, dislikes, happiness or unhappiness are determined by our lower brain, it could be argued that it is this part of the brain that is the final decision-maker.

> *A young man came into therapy feeling extremely angry with his dead father. His anger had got him into trouble with others when he was under the influence of alcohol. During such times, he would become extremely angry. Until he came for therapy, he was unaware of the reason for his anger. He used only negative words to describe his father's personality. The young man's logical conclusion*

*was that his father had destroyed his life and the life of all
of his siblings. The father was an alcoholic who became
verbally and physically violent when drunk. As the therapy
proceeded and the young man released his anger, his logic
and reasoning began to change. By the time he had fin-
ished his therapy within five or six sessions, he was able to
see the reason why his father had behaved in the way that
he did. He could appreciate the fact that his father had
come from an emotionally abusive background himself. It
was fascinating to see how the young man's own release of
negative emotions had changed his logic.*

The Cycle of Stress

To a large extent, everything in the universe is cyclical. Everything is a
part of a system. Each system has many components that follow one
after another in a cyclical pattern. As I mentioned earlier, according to
the principles of nature every cycle has some form of energy associated
with it. In an atom, when the electrons move around the nucleus, there
is an exchange of energies between the positions of the electrons. Electrons nearer the nucleus of an atom have higher energy levels compared
to electrons further away from the nucleus. The planets move around
the sun in much the same manner. The nearer the planet is to the sun the
hotter it is. All planets in the solar system move around the sun in a particular orbit as if they are maintaining their energy levels. A change in
their energy levels would theoretically change their orbits.

Loss or input of energy can affect any system: planets, governments,
families, individuals and animate and inanimate matter. In human
beings these energies have been described in terms of heat and cold.
Anger is 'hot'. Love is 'warm'. Lack of emotion is 'coldness'. Whether
or not we believe in energy exchanges, there is a constant exchange of
energy within any system of the universe. **All systems, after a threat
and a subsequent successful struggle, go through a phase of exhaustion.** This phase is significant because once it is over the energy loss is
recouped and the system comes back to normal.

Knowledge and experience give us the ability to solve problems. We
may lack this ability in certain areas and then we may perceive threat.
For example, when doing more physical work than our body can undertake normally, we can very easily experience this feeling of perceived
threat. Normally our body and our mind would have enough time in
between any kind of work to recover the lost energy. For example, over-
exertion in physical labour can result in more energy being lost than can

be recovered. When this starts to happen, the mind interprets it as a threat of danger. This lack of energy makes our mind insecure. The mind, operating unconsciously, makes the body overwork, which in turn depletes more energy and causes the brain to interpret more insecurity. Thus, the cycle of stress begins.

Diagram P: The Cycle of Stress

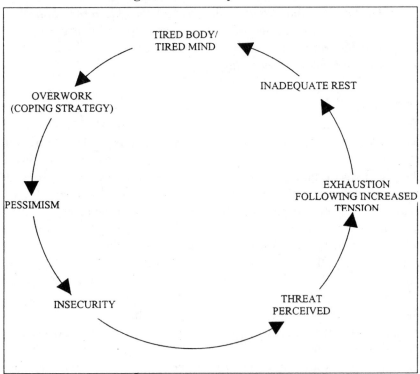

It is interesting that, as with other cycles in nature, this cycle of stress tends to perpetuate itself. The process forms an unending loop until our body dies. It is probably Nature's way to let things happen the way we perceive them to happen. As explained before, in Nature death is just a phase at which the present life ends. It is we as human beings with our limited life spans who perceive death to be the end of everything. In order to change this cycle we have an option to change only one component in the whole system. If in the *cycle of stress* we stop one component or change one cog in the whole wheel, this cycle becomes the cycle of de-stress. The cycle of de-stress generates positivity all around. Once again it is a self-perpetuating cycle. The only caution we need to have is that it can easily slip back into the *cycle of stress* when we let our guards down.

The Cycle of De-stress or the Cycle of Positivity

This cycle can start from any point in the cycle of stress. Say for example, that we can deal with our negative emotions, then our emotions become either neutral or positive. Positive emotions tend to give rise to positive thinking that also affects our perception and behaviour. Both these components of our personality become positive. Positive behaviour and positive perception once again generates more positive emotions. A positive cycle starts here.

Diagram Q: The Cycle of De-stress

REFRESHED BODY/ MIND

APPROPRIATE ACTIVITY

CREATIVITY

APPROPRIATE REST

OPTIMISM

RELAXED BODY AND MIND

FEELING OF SECURITY

It is very easy to slip from this cycle of positivity into the cycle of negativity. We can once again start from any point in the cycle. For example, if we have negative thoughts about someone we dislike, this thought of dislike will create an attitude and affect our behaviour towards that person, which will be less positive or may be negative. This in turn will generate negative responses from that person. These neg-

FOOD FOR THOUGHT
Money can provide us with physical comforts. Contentment is a state of mind. It comes free in Nature.

ative responses will reinforce our negative emotions, which will also affect and reinforce our negative perception of this person. We will then label this person as someone we do not like. The cycle continues.

Emotions, Stress and Psychotherapy

The human mind has a tendency to discern emotions as being pleasant or unpleasant. Emotions are either happy or unhappy, positive or negative. Pleasant, happy and positive emotions are comfortable. Unpleasant, unhappy and negative emotions are uncomfortable. Comfortable emotions create a de-stressed state in the mind and the body. Uncomfortable emotions create stress in the mind and the body.

In physics we learn Newton's second law. According to this law, a body will continue to remain in its state of rest or motion until an external force acts on it. This means that a body will continue to move at the same speed in the same direction until something stops it or makes it faster. Although this is a physical law, like other laws in nature, it can be seen in human life as well. We, as human beings, have a tendency to seek happiness. If possible, we would like to feel happy for our whole lives. However, daily disturbances prevent us from being happy all the time. One example of such disturbances would be the various responsibilities that we have in our lives. Unfortunately, in order to live happily we still have to fulfil those responsibilities.

> *If our life is a pond of water, then happiness can be the stillness in this pond. This is a state we all would like to achieve. A pebble thrown in the still pond disturbs the water in it. If this pebble is any form of hindrance to our happiness, then the waves created by the pebble are the emotional arousal that we have.*

The emotional arousal caused by various life occurrences has to be permitted to die out as a wave would die in the still pond. However, society has taught us that emotions are to be suppressed. "We need to get along with life." It is this attitude, coupled with our lack of skills in releasing emotions, that creates our perception of threat or stress. As days roll on into months and years, we grow up from toddlers to adults and grow into our old age. Along the way, many pebbles have been thrown into our pond of life, which after creating waves, would be still, but the waves continue and they become storms. It is at such times that others can see our perception, thinking and behaviour changing. These are the times when stress reaches that point in our lives when we start saying, "I cannot cope anymore."

At times like these, our bodies and minds become closed to all external experiences. We start focusing on our own problems, our own emotions and our own self and make ourselves mentally worked up. We create a type of mental armour around ourselves. During such states, we may become mentally ill. These illnesses are given various names by psychiatrists, for example, depression, anxiety, phobia, bipolar affective disorder, acute psychosis and schizophrenia. Whatever label is given, mental illness is caused by the accumulated effect of those unexpressed and unresolved emotions that we are trying to forget in order to 'get along with life'.

When we suffer from such conditions, all forms of psychotherapy involve helping us to become more comfortable and relaxed within ourselves. In some forms of therapy, physical relaxation is required. When the body relaxes, the mind tends to relax as well. At the moment this happens, there is a desire to release emotions. We see the pressure cooker effect here.

The pressure of emotions is so strong that the moment we let our guard down and the valve of the pressure cooker is opened, the emotions tend to escape at high pressure. This results in some patients' conditions worsening during the preliminary phases of therapy. Therapists in such situations are criticised for exacerbating their patients' illnesses. In such cases, therapists must continue to supervise their patients' release of emotions in a proper controlled manner. However, in the case of certain conditions, such as schizophrenia, the emotional pressure that is released is so huge that it is dangerous for the person, the patient and the people around the patient. This is one of the major reasons that psychotherapy has been ineffective in treating schizophrenia. Most other forms of functional psychiatric illnesses that have roots in stress can be resolved with psychotherapy.

> **FOOD FOR THOUGHT**
> **The more wants we create for ourselves, the more stressed we become.**

Stress and Nature's Principles

As I have said previously, stress is created when natural laws are flouted in any form. Nature has created a balance in all the systems that are available in the Universe. Knowledge of these systems helps us to solve problems that are created most of the time by our own selves. Whenever any imbalance is created in Nature, it tends to undo that imbalance in its own ways. More or less everything in Nature operates between two extremes. **Appreciating the two extremes and finding the middle**

Diagram R: Pressure Cooker Effect of Stress on Emotions

path is the way to de-stress any system. Between any two extremes there is a middle point. Any system that operates closer to the middle point remains alive for as long as it can maintain that position. The two extremes of any system are the birth and death of the system.

All communities, societies, countries, civilisations, planets and galaxies operate on the same principles of Nature. **When the blade of a chisel is used softly, it can carve beautiful shapes in wood and in stone. When the same blade is used with force it becomes a weapon and destroys whatever it comes into contact with.** Stress is this force that we experience when we perceive danger or threat. There is no need for us to be in physical danger in any situation for us to feel stress. For our mind, the very fact that we are running or that we are living life at a fast pace is a sign of danger. The mind interprets fast movement as meaning that we are in danger and communicates to the rest of the body to make it behave as if there is danger around us. The harder we try to convince the mind that there is no danger, the more it feels that there is danger. It ignores what we 'try' to tell it. It perceives danger from our behaviour, thoughts and emotions as they are triggered on a moment to moment basis.

Heat is a form of energy that helps us to cook food. Milder forms of heat energy in the form of natural geysers are available to us in some parts of the world. When this heat energy grows up to an extent of melting the rocks under the earth's crust, volcanoes can erupt. These volcanoes have in the past devastated civilisations. They are still capable of doing so. **The energy that we use gently is constructive for all of us. However, the same energy, when allowed to accumulate unexpressed and unreleased, becomes destructive.** It is this energy in the form of emotions, thoughts and behaviour patterns that can be destructive or can be utilised in a harsh, rude, blunt and forceful manner to cause destruction.

> **FOOD FOR THOUGHT**
> Nature is sure about producing results for our actions and thoughts. We make ourselves miserable by putting a time limit on them.

At the end of the day, all systems seek harmonisation. When a small pebble is thrown into a lake the ripples that the waves cause finally settle down. If pebble after pebble is thrown successively and quickly into the lake, the water spills over and the waves becomes more and more powerful. They take a longer time to die down. But they eventually do die. If, in the first place, we manage to stop ourselves from throwing that pebble in the pond, the lake would be stable and would remain calm. Eventually whether or not there is a pebble thrown into it, the lake will seek its calmness. That is true of human nature as well.

Signs of Stress

Any natural system, man-made system or organism when undergoing stress experiences its effects. Any such system would also show the signs of stress. In general, the signs of stress are as follows:
1. Mild – 'feeling the heat'.
2. Moderate – 'unbearable heat'.
3. Severe – 'earthquake'.

1. **Mild.** This is the first sign of stress when the individual starts 'feeling the heat'. As the system, of which the individual is a part, interacts with the individual, the individual starts becoming irritable, the mind starts racing, small mistakes are made in decision-making, the person might start feeling forgetful.

2. **Moderate.** As the individual and the environment rub against each other, the heat becomes unbearable. The individual continues to fight hoping that they will win. The harder the individual fights the stronger the opposition becomes. They become confused. There could be disturbances of sleep. As their decision-making becomes seriously flawed, mistakes become bigger. The individual may also become snappy.

3. **Severe.** This stage is like an earthquake. Things start happening in the individual's life very fast. But most of these fast happenings are destructive. The person might feel that their relationships are breaking down. Sleep and appetite are disturbed. The person may start hitting out at others or start thinking of harming themselves. Social, family and work life starts being disturbed and others start noticing it. The person may end up losing touch with reality.

By the time the person progressively moves from the mild stage to the severe stage, he or she has already made some compensatory gestures that they feel would undo the effect of the stress. In the present culture it usually takes the form of taking some form of drug, such as alcohol or medication. By the time the person shows severe signs of stress, some form of crisis has developed. Most of the time crises develop in more than one area of a person's life.

Wisdom lies in the fact that as soon as we see the first signs of stress we should start doing something about it. In fact, we would ideally have done something about it beforehand so that we do not have the signs of stress at all.

There is a trend in modern times to look at therapies and solutions to problems that are called holistic. Holistic is a very interesting word. Although it is generally assumed to refer to mind and body, it also has wider meanings. Holistic forms of work affect our social life, our family life, our body, our mind, our moods, our decision-making and our thinking processes. If therapy can be holistic, can stress be holistic? The answer is yes.

As I have discussed elsewhere, stress is a result of the interaction of the internal and or external factors. This means that when stress occurs it affects the 'environment' outside and the 'environment' inside us. The environment outside consists of our social activities, families and work. Internally, this affects the state of our mind and our body. The external environment also affects our decision-making, our ability to perceive things and our emotional responses to situations and people. Stress is holistic. What effects do stress have on a person? We must remember that stress is a perceived threat. So a stressed-out person will behave as if his or her life is in danger. This, at least, is the perception the mind – the unconscious mind – transmits to the whole body. Characteristics of a person in danger, running or fighting for his or her survival are as follows.

> **FOOD FOR THOUGHT**
> Nature has made each of us beautiful in some ways with all our imperfections.

1. **Diminished energy and interests.** Work and family become heavy burdens. Activities that one normally enjoys become chores. Energy is depleted.
2. **Complaints.** A person under stress complains more than usual. The more the person is under stress, the more they complain. From their point of view, their complaints are justified.
3. **Tone of voice.** A person who is under stress speaks in an abrupt manner. Stressed-out people speak in short, stern, soft or loud tones. In extreme stress, the person may become monosyllabic.
4. **Living elsewhere.** A stressed person finds it difficult to live in the present. The person is preoccupied either with the past or with planning for the future. This failure to live in the present is a characteristic feature of people under stress.
5. **Insecurity.** Stressed-out people are very insecure. Their insecurity also makes them more stressed out. They need to run, to act fast, and to do something that ascertains their survival. One of the most important securities that stressed-out people seek is money.

6. **Speed.** Stressed-out people usually love speed. They are people in a hurry. Their speed is indicative of their fight for survival. As they become exhausted, they slow down.

7. **Negative focusing.** Productive focusing on any work or any creation is progressive. However, a stressed-out person will focus on something that is destructive. Examples of destructive behaviours arising from a negative focus are taking revenge on someone, taking someone to court or thinking too much about one subject.

> *A middle-aged man came into therapy complaining that his handwriting had become awkward. He had become so focused on his handwriting that it had affected his work and his social life. He had developed an obsession and had to be put on medication.*

8. **Decision-making.** Decision-making becomes flawed and it may become more difficult to come to a decision.

9. **Money.** Stressed-out people are often hungry for money because of their insecurities. The more stressed a person is the hungrier they are for money. **Money provides a deceptive security to such people.**

10. **Power.** Stressed-out people are often looking for power to make them safe. They are over-ambitious people who are in a rush to do things very quickly. They are quite capable of showing streaks of extreme selfishness, because they feel to have to survive at the cost of others.

11. **Over-indulgence.** A person who is stressed-out tends to over-indulge in one or more pleasures of life. Most of the habits that people have – such as excessive drinking or excessive gambling – are examples of such over-indulgence. Over-indulgence in any activity encourages the person to avoid dealing with the other stressful issues in their life.

> *A middle-aged man was referred by his general practitioner for treatment for alcohol dependence. This person was a union leader. His parents had high expectations of him. His parents had taught him righteousness from his early years. This inhibited his freedom of thought and created emotional stress. The resulting over-arousal led him to empathise with people who were being wronged. As a result, he started fighting for the rights of people who had been wronged. He entered into a further cycle of self-perpetuating stress. This stress could be reduced by over-indulgence in alcohol, which slowed him down. A few sessions of therapy removed his insecurity. His excessive*

> *alcohol consumption stopped. It also diminished the urge to be over-active. He became a happy man.*

12. **Violence.** In situations of extreme stress, people are more likely to become violent. When stressed, we perceive danger where it does not exist. In order to deal with danger, Nature provides us with brute strength before we become violent. **As we become more and more stressed, the obstacles that prevent us from resorting to violence start to diminish. We reach a stage at which we become violent with very little provocation.** A stressed-out violent person looks at violence as the *only* way to deal with any situation. Moreover, it is the first choice that the person has.

> *An angry man suppressed his anger against his father. This continued until he started to develop a dependence on alcohol. A pattern of behaviour was established in which he would get drunk and become verbally and physically violent towards others. Otherwise, he was a very decent person. As his anger was released during therapy, his alcohol consumption diminished. He later reported that consuming alcohol no longer made him verbally and physically violent.*

13. **Inflated ego.** Our fears contribute to our inherent insecurities. These insecurities make us seek more and more attention from others. People with inflated egos are actually stressed-out people. The more we seek attention, the more we need it. We enter into the cycle of self-perpetuation of stress. The moment someone gives us less attention, we start feeling hurt. Egotistical people belong to this category of stressed-out persons.

14. **Control.** The more a person is stressed-out, the more insecure the person becomes. This insecurity leads a person to seek control. This results in behaviour that some people have described as 'trying to take control'. The harder the person tries to control events and their own life, the more energy they have to spend and the more stressed-out they become.

15. **Selfishness.** Selfishness involves looking after one's self while ignoring others. Selfish people are inconsiderate. However, selfishness is a relative term. People can be more or less selfish. Selfishness enables a person to do things for one's own survival at the cost of others.

16. **Illness.** Stressed-out people have a higher intensity and a higher frequency of illness – both physical and mental. Many physical disorders are related to our psychological state. Crohn's Disease,

ulcerative colitis and irritable bowel syndrome have been shown to be stress-related. Many skin disorders, including psoriasis and warts, are also stress-related.

17.**Emotional arousal.** Emotional arousal that occurs suddenly is a sign of internal stress. The more easily aroused a person is, the more stressed the person becomes. The ability to be aroused emotionally is different from being emotionally sensitive.

18.**Values and beliefs.** A stressed-out person has a very rigid value and belief system. Sometimes they may have delusions. A delusion is described as a belief, usually false, that is out of keeping with the person's social, cultural and educational background. The more rigid the person becomes, the harder it is to reason with that person. This is irrespective of whether the value or belief is right or wrong. The intensity of rigidity the person has for the belief, which is in an indicator of stress.

19.**Telling lies.** A stressed-out person finds it easier to tell lies. In other words, people who tell lies are under stress. Telling lies is a habit that comes from some form of fear. Fear is a conditioned response in some situations where our survival is at stake. Once it becomes a habit, a person is totally unaware of why he or she tells lies.

20.**Over-stimulation and under-stimulation.** When we are stressed-out, we tend either to over-stimulate or under-stimulate ourselves. Once again, we enter into a self-perpetuating cycle of increasing stress, this time through over-stimulation. Listening to loud music for a long time or engaging in other activities that involve over-stimulation of our senses can result in stress. On the other hand, when we feel low we under-stimulate ourselves and go into a cycle of under-stimulation that may result in depression. This may in turn cause a threat to our own lives.

21.**Focus.** The more stressed we become the more we tend to focus on one aspect ourselves and of our lives. It becomes more and more difficult for us to distract ourselves from that focus.

Anxieties, phobias, depression, obsessive compulsive behaviour and some forms of psychosis come from stress that is perpetuated by and perpetuates focused attention. An anxious person may be focused on the future; a depressed person may be focused on the past. An obsessive-compulsive person would be focused on a particular thought or process. A psychotic person may become focused on a paranoid idea or a person or situation.

The more the person focuses on something the more difficult it becomes to distract them from that attention. Incidentally, some forms of therapy encourage distraction techniques to relieve stress.

Stress is Infectious

> *A professional, who was struggling with his practice, noticed that he was becoming more stressed when he went home. His wife had learned that her sister who lived abroad had recently been diagnosed with a psychosis. This was seen as being shameful for the family and had affected his wife, who was close to her sister. When he would arrive home from work, his wife would complain to him about various issues. She would threaten to leave because her life with him had become unbearable. This man found himself under pressure as a result.*

This is a classic example of stress in one person affecting others. **Stress, like emotions, is self-perpetuating and infectious.** If we feel low at any time, a cheerful friend can cheer us up. A gloomy or angry person can make us more depressed.

Whenever two people meet, there is often an unconscious struggle between their mood states. If one of them is happy and the other unhappy, depending on the strength of their emotion, one of them can overpower the other person's emotions. If one is unhappy and the strength of this unhappiness is more powerful than the strength of the happiness of the other person, then the happy person will become unhappy. Similarly, if the unhappiness is of a transient nature and the happiness of the other person is more powerful, then the happy person can successfully cheer up the unhappy person. It is fascinating to observe that all of us want to be happy and that we unconsciously seek the company of others who can make us happy. We unconsciously affect each other's emotional states. **Stress is transmitted, not only from person to person, but also from generation to generation, affecting our belief systems and our values.**

> *An insecure and fearful young man coming from a deprived background was admitted to a drug-treatment centre. Since the treatment was in-patient, there were rules laid down that non-prescribed or street drugs were to stay out of the admission unit. This young man had been brought up in such a stressful environment throughout his life that being truthful and honest was against his value system. He brought cannabis from outside into the unit.*

Another patient complained about it to the doctors. A strict view was taken of this incident. The young man was asked to leave the unit. He failed to appreciate that he had done something wrong which had affected other people's welfare. Deception, telling lies and stealing were integral parts of his belief system.

Rule of Thumb
We do damage to self, others or the environment
only under conditions of stress. As we become de-stressed,
we become more constructive

Transactional analysis is a method of therapy developed by an American psychiatrist, Eric Berne. He postulated that each of us has a 'parent', an 'adult' and a 'child' in us. All of us have these parts that manifest themselves – as a parent, an adult or as a child – at any given moment in time. The dominance of any of these parts in our life depends on what has been recorded in our mind. Our mind functions like a tape recorder. It repetitively plays back the emotions and thoughts that have been recorded in our brains by our parents. The recording determines if we are dominated by 'parent' thinking, 'adult' thinking or 'child' thinking. It also affects our behaviour as adults. We continue to play the same tape throughout life until a new recording is made on the tape. Emotions tend to play a very significant role in these recordings. If the emotions are negative, they generate stress. So if our upbringing has been mostly stressful, we continue to lead stressful lives till we die. One way to change this pattern and escape from a stressful life is to go through a therapeutic process.

A man who had abused a close relative came for treatment voluntarily. He regretted what he had done. He said he had no clue why he had done what he had done but he felt totally responsible for his actions. He had come into therapy to deal with the issues that had made him an abuser. His history revealed that he had been emotionally, physically and sexually abused himself. His responsible position in society was unhelpful in helping him resolve his emotional problems. He eventually worked through his emotional stressors successfully.

When we come across people who are stressed out, their stress may infect us. We can pick on the stress and unknowingly pass on this stress to others. In one sense, we can blame others for putting us under stress.

On the other hand, we can take responsibility ourselves for being infected by their stress. By doing this, we can activate ways to deal with our own stresses. This helps us to deal with our stresses and ensures that we stop passing on these stresses to others.

How we can Diminish Stress

Understanding this connection between stressors inside us and stressors outside us enables us to appreciate how we can control our environment. From time immemorial, wise people have stated repeatedly that we control our destinies, that we control our environment and that we can change many things around us without making much effort. In order to understand this concept, we need to refer to some of the topics discussed earlier in this book.

The stress that we experience physically and mentally is the net result of the interaction between internal stressors that are inside us and external stressors that are outside us. Internal stressors include emotions that we carry within ourselves, which have been there from when we were young. These emotions condition us to think and behave in a particular pattern. According to psychologist George Kelly and others, we tend to have "schemas" in our mind with which we compare the input of information that comes to us. Kelly proposed that our mind operates in a predictable way. Our learning creates sets of information or "schemas" in our mind with which we compare any new information that reaches our mind. If the new information matches the "schema" already there in the mind, we accept it. If the information does not match any pre-set "schema", we reject it. The difficulty in accepting new information that is out of step with old "schemata" causes stress. External stressors are the conditions that are around us in our family, at work and in social situations. In order for stress to occur, an interaction between these internal and external stressors has to occur.

There are cues in our environment that arouse our emotions and affect our thinking. This interaction between the factors that are within us and without us stimulates our mind. This stimulation is a conditioned response to our past experiences, which are usually emotional. This conditioning is like a network that has been set up in our minds. This network consists of nerve cells that conduct nerve or electrical impulses. This stimulation of the nerve cells occurs in a set pattern. This pattern creates a set process of thinking and a set method of behaviour. This is all learnt due to conditioning, which has been discussed earlier in the chapter. As this thinking and behaviour is set in a particular manner, it limits our thoughts and behaviours. Unknown to us, this pattern is repeated throughout our whole lives. When we are under stress we tend to look at external factors that have put us under stress. We blame our work, lack of money, our spouses, our children, our bosses, the driver driving in front or the bureaucrat that we think is slowing things down.

In order to change this pattern of stress, we can change our external environment. However, there are limits to this type of solution. We can change our job, but it is sometimes impossible to change our boss. We can change our house, but it is sometimes impossible to change our spouse. We cannot change or exchange our children. Therefore, changing the environment around us has a limited value.

Fortunately, we can change our internal environment as well. **As our bodies and our minds work together, making any changes in our thinking processes, our behaviours or our internal emotional states, can change our responses to the environment.** If the environment remains stressful, but we change our emotional state or responses, then stress can be reduced and ultimately eliminated.

How Stress Affects our Memory

Until recently, neuroscientists were under the impression that our memory was confined to a particular part of the brain. Later they started to believe that our whole brain participates in memory processes. The most recent research and publications have revealed that memory is available to us in each and every cell of our body. As our whole body works as one unit, making changes in one part of our body, affects all the other parts and organs of the body. For example, if someone has cancer in any part of their body, their whole body responds as if it is working towards dealing with that cancer. All of the systems in their body are affected by the presence of the cancer. Our mind also responds to this condition. Cancer patients often suffer from depression, which is a mental condition.

FOOD FOR THOUGHT When we want something, we pay for it to get it. When we "need" something, we could do anything for it.

Our bodies are mainly composed of water and proteins that make up most of the solids. Proteins are made from amino acids. Proteins are formed when 200 or more amino acids join each other in the form of a chain. Neuropeptides are formed when 100 or so amino acids link together. These neuropeptides are present in every part of our body. Each emotional experience helps produce a specific type of neuropeptide. These neuropeptides directly affect the parts of the cells that are called receptors. Receptors and neuropeptide ligands are both made from amino acids. They fit into each other in the same way as a lock and key. Each emotional experience sets a pattern of these ligands, which affect their specific receptors on cells in each and every part of our body. Every time we undergo an experience, it arouses certain emotions in us. These emotions seem to reactivate interactions between the ligands and receptors. Every time we undergo similar emotional experiences, these ligand receptor interactions are reinforced repetitively. This sets a pattern of conditioned emotional experiences. In other words, we learn to behave emotionally through conditioning. Conditioning is a learnt behaviour that we exhibit at an unconscious level.

A classic example of conditioned or learnt behaviour is the way we develop fears or phobias. If a person is afraid of cats, then every time the person even looks at a picture of a cat, it arouses certain emotions in the body. This emotion is that of fear and it is activated through the neuropeptide linkages and ligand-receptor interaction. Each time the fear of cats is aroused, the same interaction is reinforced. This conditions the whole body to respond in a particular manner to a picture of a cat. Conditioning in this case arouses fear, which is an emotion that ensures the survival of the individual. The person either runs away or avoids the source of fear as a result. During such experiences, the whole body is geared towards running away.

We can also explain the above phenomenon through electrical conduction theory. If our nervous system conducts messages in the form of electrical impulses, then seeing a cat through our eyes triggers something in our brain that switches on these electrical impulses. Repetitive arousal of emotions, with repetitive neuropeptide linked receptor interaction of a similar nature, probably sets a pattern. This pattern may be in the form of electrical pathways through which electrical conduction occurs whenever the emotion of fear is aroused on seeing a cat or the picture of a cat. This creates a thinking pattern that becomes stereotyped. It is theoretically impossible to make a change in this whole pattern. Something seems to happen during this process of emotional arousal, fear, neuropeptide activity and ligand-receptor interaction that becomes a part of our memory.

Neurologists are aware that our higher or thinking or cognitive brain has connections with the deeper part of the brain that affects our emotions and also with the spinal chord and the rest of our body. Messages are transferred from a remote part of the body, say for example, a toe, to reach the cerebral cortex. This is a two-way pathway as information is also transmitted from the cerebral cortex to the toe. Theoretically speaking, our toe can learn about *any* information that has come into the cerebral cortex, just as the cerebral cortex can become aware, through the transmission of messages, that the toe has been hurt. This is a very interesting phenomenon that has been knowingly or unknowingly used in various forms of therapy that include alternative or complementary therapy and modern medicine. This will be discussed later in this book.

5. THE LONG-TERM EFFECTS OF STRESS

So far, we have discussed the effects of stress on a short-term basis. We have also discussed the signs that we see in an individual who has undergone physical or mental stress of any kind. Stress not only affects the individual but can also affect the whole of society, the whole country and future generations.

> *A married businesswoman, the mother of grown-up children, came into therapy. She was a controlling person. She had reared all her children, working very hard to bring them up. However, she now used alcohol as a way of coping with life. Her middle-aged daughter had remained unmarried but had made a lot of money controlling her own life and other people. The mother's mother had been a controlling woman in her own right. She herself had raised many children under very difficult circumstances. This lady had controlled her whole family and her husband with an iron fist. The grandmother of the patient was also a very controlling woman. Probably she had had a rough time in her own childhood. It was fascinating to see this person, the patient, changing in therapy, working through her emotions. She developed insight to see that there was a set pattern in the behaviours, thinking processes and emotional responses in four generations in her family. She could appreciate what stress had done to all of them.*

This is one example of the many instances in which stressful patterns of emotions, thinking behaviour and perception are repeated in succeeding generations. Eric Berne, the noted psychiatrist, in his description of transactional analysis, describes the tape that is played for the rest of our lives after it is recorded during the first six years of our rearing. Our initial rearing tapes the messages that we get from our caregivers. The caregivers (usually parents) have their own tapes in their heads, recorded by their own caregivers. Stress can be passed on from one generation to the next generation, unknown to us.

> *A general practitioner referred a patient suffering from depression for treatment. This patient had recently suffered a heart attack. On speaking to the patient's wife on the phone, I became aware that the patient had been a very*

*angry man throughout his life. As the patient was bed-rid-
den, and had recently been through an acute, life-threaten-
ing situation, his physical recovery was of primary
importance and had to be dealt with before therapy could
be undertaken. The wife of the patient stated that she
would contact the therapist again for treatment once the
patient began leading a normal life. After a few weeks I
learned from the general practitioner that the patient had
died. He had passed away without having the opportunity
to work on his anger at all.*

Some of the long-term effects of stress that can be passed on from generation to generation are:
a) physical and psychosomatic illnesses;
b) mental illnesses;
c) addictions;
d) eating disorders;
e) abuse;
f) complaining and blaming;
g) obsessions;
h) child rearing;
i) religious or political fanaticism;
j) racism;
k) affairs in the workplace;
l) decision-making;
m) family life;
n) corruption.

When we are threatened we feel insecure. We want to save ourselves
even if this means harming others. Physically, we become smaller than
before. Our thinking also becomes 'small'. Our actions become mean
and selfish. We become more cunning. We become stressed. We start
suffering from physical ailments. Skin disorders are the commonest
physical expressions of mental stress.

When we become de-stressed, all of the above effects tend to disap-
pear. Changes that are brought about by de-stressing ourselves are discussed elsewhere.

Physical and Psychosomatic Illness

In this section, I list some of the physical illnesses that have their roots
in psychological stress. Such illnesses are:

a) **gastrointestinal disorders** – dysphagia (difficulty in swallowing), peptic ulcer disease, non-ulcer dyspepsia, irritable bowel syndrome, ulcerative colitis, Crohn's disease;

b) **respiratory illnesses** – bronchial asthma, hyperventilation syndrome;

c) **cardiovascular illnesses** – hypertension (elevated blood pressure), coronary artery disease;

d) **skin disorders** – acne, eczema (also called dermatitis), psoriasis, urticaria, pruritus;

e) **immune disorders** – rheumatoid arthritis, AIDS, cancers can be exacerbated by stress;

f) **headaches** – tension headache, migraine.

Mental Illness

Mental illnesses can occur with or without any brain damage. Brain damage occurs when we experience a violent accident or trauma, following a head injury. Head injury affects a person's appearance, behaviour, speech, emotional reactivity, mood state, thought processes, perception, cognition and insight. These can be affected by prolonged stress. Some types of mental illness that are caused by prolonged stress are:

a) **mood disorders** – depression, manic depression (bipolar affective disorder);

b) **anxiety disorders** – phobias (including agoraphobia), panic disorders, post-traumatic stress disorder, obsessive-compulsive disorder;

c) **somatoform disorders** – somatization disorders, conversion disorder, hypochondriasis;

d) **schizophrenia** – schizophrenia and related illnesses, acute psychosis;

e) **sleep disorders** – insomnia, hypersomnia;

f) **sexual dysfunction** – ejaculatory dysfunction, vaginismus, dyspareunia.

Addictions, habit disorders and eating disorders are also stress-related illnesses. These are discussed below.

Addictions

Any need that we create for ourselves, which is non-vital and which at some point in our life becomes the primary need, for which we can ignore or neglect everything else, is an addiction.

According to the above definition, all forms of drug dependence are addictions. Even falling in love would fit into the above definition.

Some people can become addicted to sex; others become addicted to drugs. Dependence on prescribed and non-prescribed drugs, indulging in any physical over-activity, living in a painful relationship and not being able to live without it, looking for different partners for sexual activity and becoming involved in abusive relationships are all signs of addictions. All addictions give us a sense of happiness. Some of these addictions are stimulating, whereas others slow us down. Various addictive drugs fall into similar categories. People who have addictions are unconsciously looking for balance in their lives. This balance is achieved, however transiently, by indulging in the addictive habit, addictive behaviour or addictive drug.

> *A young bus driver was assaulted while on duty. The driver developed symptoms of post-traumatic stress disorder. He began to indulge in addictive behaviours, one of which was bodybuilding for many hours everyday. Following treatment, his addictive behaviour resolved.*

Sex addiction is classified in the *International Classification of Diseases, 10th edition (ICD 10)* as "excessive sexual drive". The term addiction would hardly be used if the excessive sexual drive occurs between two partners in a long-term relationship. It becomes an addiction when it starts affecting many people's lives, when the addict looks for different sexual partners. It usually happens at the cost of a lot of financial, physical and emotional difficulty. Such an addiction has affected many political lives. (It is quite common to see stress among politicians.)

> *A highly stressed-out middle-aged man complained of excessive sexual drive outside marriage for a major part of his life. He had been unhappily married. This had resulted in his seeking multiple partners outside marriage. His wife of many years was totally unaware of his activities. There were many issues in his childhood that had been left unresolved. These issues were related to the fact that he was brought up by multiple pairs of parents. He was a very fearful, insecure man. Interestingly, as his emotional issues were resolved within a few meetings, the frequency of his visits to prostitutes dropped dramatically.*

Smoking is one of the most common addictions. Billions of pounds worth of cigarettes are smoked in Europe and America annually. Smoking provides our blood stream and circulatory system with a chemical called nicotine, which is a stimulant. Our body and our mind need more stimulation when we are under threat or perceived danger. This stimulation provides energy for us to fight the perceived danger. **The more stressed-out we are the more we smoke. The less stressed-out and more relaxed we are, the less we smoke.**

I have worked with many people in therapy settings whose primary complaint was different from smoking but who were smokers. They all had different complaints, related to chronic stress. As therapy progressed, some of them reported a fall in their desire to smoke cigarettes. Later, they all reported a dramatic decrease in their cigarette smoking.

Relaxation techniques and hypnosis have been long known to help people to give up smoking. Alternative nicotine products are useful and helpful, but they do little to help a person de-stress and eliminate the core problem of stress.

Drugs that are misused are categorised as 'uppers' (stimulants), 'downers' (depressants), or 'hallucinogens'. Uppers or downers can be habit-forming but hallucinogens are not. If our life is stress free, we need hardly any 'uppers' or 'downers' to help us regain our 'equanimity' or 'balance'. People use these drugs in order to regain a balance or 'to cope'. When our parents have separated, or when we feel lonely, or when we have been abused, we spontaneously feel low and may become clinically depressed. During such times, usage of stimulant drugs or 'uppers' may help us. Amphetamines and cocaine are examples of such stimulant drugs. When life becomes so stressful that a person has to be ready to fight all the time, there is a perpetual muscular and mental tension. This chronic muscular and mental tension leads a person to start abusing 'downers' or depressants. Opiate drugs are typical examples of such 'downers'. Among the 'abused' downers that are prescribed are benzodiazepines. Hallucinogens are unpredictable in that they can act as stimulants and/or depressants, depending on the initial mood-state of the person. All of these drugs affect our nervous system. Prolonged usage of these drugs makes us dependent on them and they become our *need*. This need drives us to think and behave in unpredictable ways. Even our perception changes. More and more time and energy is spent seeking avenues to fulfil this need. Other productive and constructive activities take a back seat. Our personalities take a downturn and we degenerate mentally.

> **FOOD FOR THOUGHT**
> If everything in Nature was perfect, there would hardly be anything beautiful.

Most of the treatments dealing with drug misuse and abuse emphasise the importance of changing external stressors. There are various social welfare outlets and facilities that are available to people who misuse drugs. Replacement of the misused drugs with legalised dependence is also promoted. However, there is a limited emphasis on eliminating internal stressors. Psychotherapeutic procedures that would help a person to deal with such internal stressors can be quite fast and economical. They help people to gain confidence and can enable them to become self-dependent. Such procedures usually require specialised skills. Almost all addictions have negative emotions as integral and mandatory components of the problem.

Habit disorders, such as pathological lying and gambling, that cause harm to the person, the family members and the society at large are also due to chronic stress. Insecurity, low self-esteem, neglect or rejection by caregivers (including parents) contributes to a person seeking alternative avenues of security and safety. Negative emotions related to low self-esteem cause a person to become fearful and resort to lying. Lying is a survival activity. People in a hurry to make money resort to gambling. **We are in a hurry when we are under stress.** Gamblers are under stress and feel unsafe without money. Because they have to regain the money that they have lost in previous gambling activities, they have to gamble again and again to recoup the lost money. This initiates a cycle of stress that is self-perpetuating. This cycle eventually leads to a loss of self-esteem and to feelings of insecurity. The removal of internal emotional stressors in such cases would eliminate the need to indulge in this harmful activity.

Rule of Thumb
When coming off any addiction, drink plenty of water.

Weight Problems and Eating Disorders

These disorders, if not related to any genetic or physical condition, are almost always stress-related. Some eating disorders, such as bulimia, may not be weight-related at all. Stress comprises both physical and mental tension. Our mind perceives this mental tension as a form of threat. This threat means that we are going to lose or have already lost control over our own lives. The choice that an organism has during such situations is either to fight the threat or to run away. Both these activities are physically exhausting activities that require energy. Energy is provided to us by food. Food, in turn, is classified according to the need that it fulfils for our body. During stressful activities, most of the foods that we eat are energy giving foods. Food can be energy giving or bodybuilding or can help to maintain body functions. Carbohydrates are the commonest energy giving foods and these are rapidly digested and absorbed in the body. All sugars and cereals come under this classification. People who overeat and are obese as a result eat mainly carbohydrates or fried food. Therefore, overeating fulfils the need for more energy our bodies create due to stress.

A corollary to the above explanation of overeating is that we would eat less if we were relaxed and de-stressed. Theoretically, this is possible. When a person is relaxed, de-stressed, self-assured and self-confident, their mind is calm. This calmness obviates the need to eat more energy foods to fight any threat or danger. The person then eats appropriately and their weight remains reasonable.

> *A young married woman came into therapy looking for help for her overeating. Her mother had died a few years previously and the young woman subsequently had gained weight. She realised she was eating more chocolates than usual but could hardly help herself. On completion of grief therapy, she stopped eating chocolates and other sweet products spontaneously. Within the next few months her weight came back to normal.*

Another patient who was much older confirmed a similar experience.

> *A lady in her late 50s reported for therapy. She was advised to do a relaxation exercise on a regular basis spending a stipulated amount of time every day. Within a few weeks of doing this exercise, she reported that she had noticed a decline in her weight. She was delighted with the result because she always wanted to lose some weight but "had no time for it".*

In anorexia and bulimia, there is a distortion of body image. These illnesses occur due to increased stress, which makes a person a 'control freak'. The person uses their energies to control their life, including their weight. Most of the people suffering from anorexia or bulimia suffer from some kind of 'pressure'. This 'pressure' or stress is interpreted as a threat by the brain. As these people perceive their lives to be getting out of control, they make more and more attempts to regain control. This sets off a vicious cycle in which stress is increased rather than decreased. These conditions are rooted in an underlying emotional disturbance. This disturbance leaves a person feeling unsafe and vulnerable. **The more the person tries to gain control, the less control they actually gain.** Most of the time, the underlying emotion is fear, anger or both.

Abuse

Abuse is a widespread phenomenon all over the world, it has come into prominence more and more during recent years as stresses in life have been increasing. Developments in communications, education, awareness of abuse in the media and acknowledgement of abuse by the professions have all contributed to its exposure. Abuse can be sexual, physical or emotional. All sexual abuse involves sexual, physical and emotional abuse. All physical abuse involves physical and emotional abuse. Emotional abuse can stand alone without physical or sexual abuse. Neglect, rejection or threats are forms of emotional abuse.

Abuse is misuse of power. Anyone in a higher position of authority or power can cause sexual, physical or emotional damage in a dependent, weaker or subordinate person. Any form of abuse creates stress in the abused. As discussed earlier, stress is infectious. Therefore, an abused person who is under stress has the potential of doing damage to others as well. Interestingly, most abuse is carried out by people who have been abused themselves. Most sexual abuse is perpetrated by people who have been either sexually, physically or emotionally abused themselves. A de-stressed person would have lesser chances of abusing others.

As with everything else, we give to others what we have. If we have money in abundance, we can spend and give away money. If we have abundant knowledge, we can give it to others. If we have happiness in ourselves, we give it to others unconsciously. If we have stress in ourselves, we give it to others unconsciously. An abused person is a stressed-out person. They may give to others is abuse – verbal, physical or emotional.

> *A middle-aged businessman had sexually abused a young, female acquaintance. This person had no previous history of abusing anyone. He was leading a happy married life. During therapy, it became apparent that he had himself been sexually abused. He had never previously talked of or discussed this with anyone and had thought that he had 'forgotten' this experience. He also had a demanding father who had put him under stress. His current lifestyle was very busy so that he had hardly any time alone to deal with his emotional difficulties. In fact, he thought he had none. As he worked through his emotional negative past, his attitude towards women also started to change. He unconsciously felt less need for the attention-seeking behaviour that he had previously exhibited. Finally, he was*

advised to de-stress himself on a regular basis daily to
make sure that he would remain in control of his life, and
his behaviour.

Complaining and Blaming

All of us have come across people who complain a lot and blame others
for nearly everything that goes wrong. Such people are usually bitter
and angry. One of their most common complaints is that others do not
understand them. (This is a common complaint among adolescents
when they have difficulties with their parents.) Such complaints, though
usually genuine, are followed by verbal assaults on others. These are the
people who have suffered stress at the hands of their parents, caregivers
or people in authority.

Such people are so bitter and angry that they can easily become paranoid if they become fearful. If such people were to deal with their negative emotions, they could be very constructive individuals. Letting go
of their negative emotions would also help them to become happier and
contented in themselves.

Obsessions

An obsession is a thought or idea that comes into a person's mind
repeatedly despite the person making an effort to dispel this thought or
idea. **It is a form of hypnotic state in which a person becomes
focused on something – an idea, a thought or a person. Obsession
occurs when we become insecure.** We are unhappy about our own
existence, so, unknown to ourselves, we focus attention on something
outside of us and continue to think about it.

Stalking is a classic example of how an obsession can affect a person's behaviour. A stalker is usually an insecure, fearful individual who
is isolated. A stalker is very unhappy. Theoretically, possession of the
object of stalking would solve the problem for this person. However,
this is not the case. If the stalker is prosecuted or arrested for a stalking
offence, their inherent insecurity and low self-esteem and isolated lifestyle remain unchanged. All of these factors are known stressors. Once
again, it is the interaction between the internal stressors the person suffers from and their external environment that makes the person insecure
and creates stress. The answer to this problem would be to release those
emotions that have made this person insecure and obsessed.

Obsessions and compulsions are related. In order to avoid thinking
about something, a person will usually initiate an activity that distracts
them from this thought. This type of activity is called a compulsion. A

compulsion, like an obsessional thought, is repetitive in nature. Checking, counting, and cleaning are three common repetitive, compulsive rituals. In order to deal with an obsessional thought, the best way is to busy oneself in an activity. This is an outlet for a person who is insecure inside and has low self-esteem.

> *A young mother of a baby girl was referred for obsessional thoughts with regard to this little baby's genitals. This young mother had sexual thoughts about harming this little baby girl's genitals. The thought had become so obsessional and powerful that in her effort to fight them or to expel them out of her mind she became depressed. Her fight with these thoughts was unsuccessful. She was a very good mother and continued to look after the child to her best ability. Luckily for her, she never harmed the child despite undergoing this experience. Working through her insecurity and her emotional difficulties with her own mother developed insight in her. She realised that after all it was 'just a thought', like any other thought, and that she was as good a mother as she could be. This took pressure away from her mind. Her internal stressors diminished. The same environment that was previously stressful for her became comfortable. Her relationship with her husband improved as well.*

Child Rearing

This is one of the most difficult areas of human life. Yet, most of the people in the world go through this process without any training. Unfortunately, there is hardly any right way to rear children. Most parents feel that they have done their best for their child or children.

It is fascinating when working as a therapist to watch how generations are affected by the same emotional experiences. **Generations of people coming from a family have the same patterns of behaviour, thinking and perception about the world around them.** Probably this is what makes cultures. But each family has its own culture or traditions. An American family would have a different tradition or culture than another family living in the same neighbourhood, coming from a different background. The emotional experiences and stimuli that arouse individuals, interestingly, remain similar in families for generations.

> *Coming from a physically violent background, a middle-aged man wanted to do 'something' about his problems.*

His problems were numerous. He had five children all of whom had been leading unhappy lives in some form or the other. He did not get along with any of them. One of the sons had even beaten him up at one stage. None of the sons lived with him and his wife. He gave his history, hiding the fact that he had been physically abusive to his own children when they were growing up. It was revealed later that his father had also had a very difficult upbringing. He had come from a very strict background, and so, in turn, he had brought up his son in an extremely restrictive, physically abusive environment.

This example shows how anger can be passed from generation to generation and affects the life of each and every individual in the family. This can happen with any such emotion. Unknown to the man in the story, he was driving his children away from himself because of his behaviour, which was quite violent. It was fascinating that he could not see that his own violence came from his upbringing and that this was being passed on to the next generation.

When a man and a woman mate to bring a baby into this world, they usually put in all their energies into bringing up the child. These energies are sexual energies, social energies, financial energies and emotional energies. The last is usually ignored. Each parent comes from a different emotional pool. When they come together and bring the child into the world, they pool their emotional energies into their own family. These emotional energies affect the baby. Unknown to the parents or the baby, the emotional energies start affecting this baby's life from the time he or she is born. The emotions set off patterns of stimuli and responses to each and every sound, experience and vision that the baby has. All five senses are involved to set a pattern of emotional arousal, thinking, behaviour and perception. There are set patterns of regaining emotional balance when the baby gets emotionally aroused. Even problem solving or problem avoidance has a set pattern. The child might learn, for instance, that when a problem cannot be dealt with, then the person should leave home. The other alternative could be to start drinking in excess. Other alternatives could be to deal with the problem at hand there and then by discussing the matter with concerned people or to take a break and go away for a holiday. When this child grows up to be an adult, they carry their own emotional pool everywhere they go. It is interesting that the child, now an adult, is spontaneously going to pick a mate who will have very similar problems and patterns of behaviour and thinking as they have. Once again they will fulfil each other's emotional needs. Carrying their genes and their emotions they could invest whatever they have, to bring up another young person, passing on their family rituals of thinking, behaviour, perception and emotions.

The responsibility of dealing with our stresses and our internal stressors rests with us. We are responsible for passing on our emotional baggage to the next generation. Very ambitious parents often put a lot of stress on their children. This stress is usually internalised. These children might be able to achieve high social status and power and attain a lot of wealth but, at the end of the day, they lose their happiness. The balance in their lives is lost, usually permanently. If a child's parents lay emphasis on expression, on happiness and on achievement, which usually comes with consistency rather than with intensity, a child grows up to be a happy adult. This child can easily attain whatever he or she wants.

> **FOOD FOR THOUGHT**
> The harder we 'try' to control everything in life, the more tension is created in our bodies and minds. We lose more and more control as a result.

Religious and Political Fanaticism

When any religion becomes insecure, it becomes controlling. The same is true with political parties. **Whenever there is a threat to any system, the system becomes withdrawn and compact.** It is the same response that an individual has whenever he or she is threatened. We roll ourselves into a ball and make ourselves smaller and more insignificant. Withdrawing from the normal stream of life hides the insecurity that such people usually feel. However, this insecurity can be dangerous. It usually takes the form of fear and an animal who is in fear of something retaliates violently. All human beings are seeking to work towards their own happiness. Nature has also given us freedom – freedom of expression, freedom to scream and shout, freedom to express our emotions in a controlled way. When fear is instilled into a person or a group of people, it breeds insecurity, which causes problems for other peace-loving citizens of any country. The term 'extremism' is commonly used to describe the attitude of such groups. Extremism, in turn, creates another natural response and this response is one of opposition. In order to oppose this extremism, other forces have to become powerful as well and once again stressors and stresses start following each other in cyclical patterns.

It is interesting that in any political or religious organisation that is insecure, we look for the 'moderates' – people who can find the middle path or the 'balanced path'. **At the end of the day, it is the balance in any system and in individuals that brings about peace, prosperity and happiness.**

Racism

It is fascinating to watch racist organisations and their members on television. The most interesting point to note is that these people have forgotten to smile. Such people look stern and aggressive. Their eyes are focused and they look angry. Their bodies are tense and so are their minds. Such people are so stressed out with insecurity and fear that their best choice is to be offensive towards others. This tendency to be offensive can be in mild form or it can be in more severe forms, involving threatening or actually harming the life of other people. Most racists come from very insecure and fearful upbringings. Such people usually come from poor backgrounds and deprived conditions. They are indeed very unhappy people. Once again they follow simple patterns of Nature. They give to others what they have within themselves – dislike, hatred and unhappiness. They have their own internal stressors that rub against the external environment (in which maybe the opportunities are few as they see it) and so they become stressed out and fearful of others.

Affairs in the Workplace

Affairs in the workplace and sexual harassment are common problems for both employees and employers. These activities lead to unhappiness for everyone. Most of these activities take place when people are stressed out. **When people feel insecure, they look for attention.** When they are fearful of their employment, their self-esteem becomes low, and they then tend to seek to release tension through sexual activities. A de-stressed, relaxed person would hardly care to indulge in any of these activities. De-stressed individuals have appropriate self-esteem and have control over their actions. Such people are usually happy and secure in themselves.

Stress creates stress. Stress is usually accompanied by a state of emotional arousal. Such arousal requires emotional release of some kind. Once emotions are aroused, they find their release in some behaviour.

> *Mr A and Ms B used to work in an office together. They were in the same position of responsibility. Mr A was single. Ms B was married. Their work involved staying overtime in office. Their work was challenging. They had to meet deadlines. Their boss, Mr C, was also a stressed-out,*

tough individual, who was pushing both Mr A and Ms B to
get results. Ms B was newly married but had little time to
be with her new husband. One day Ms B had a harsh
exchange of words with the boss, Mr C. She came back to
her own cabin to find Mr A ready to sympathise with her. A
few days later, Ms B was telling Mr A how difficult life was
with her husband. Mr A also had difficult times with Mr C
at work. A few days later, there was a party after work.
Both Mr A and Ms B were at the party. They had their first
intimate encounter at that time. An affair had started.

Sex releases physical and emotional tension. Under stress, we tend inadvertently to drift into sexual activity in order to gain emotional release. The likelihood of someone being involved in such affairs depends on their own background and their stress levels. These affairs are especially likely to occur when any other stress-release mechanism is unavailable. Needless to say, such affairs have powerful impact on many people's lives.

Family Life

All of us have internal stressors. These internal stressors, in the form of our emotional experiences and negative emotional baggage, have set out a pattern of thinking and behaviour. Our attitude towards this baggage is important when we deal with these internal stressors. **If we believe that there is nothing that we can do about these stressors, we do nothing to change them.** By taking responsibility for dealing with those internal stressors so that we become less stressed out, we find that life outside of us changes.

Our emotional baggage affects many aspects of our lives. We enter into relationships carrying this baggage with us. Most of the time, we find someone who can complement our emotional baggage with whom to start a relationship or a family. The emotional energies that we put into dealing with our family affect the happiness or unhappiness of the family. Our set patterns of thinking, behaviour and problem-solving on a daily basis determine what the next generation learns from us. **Dysfunctional families produce dysfunctional children. Functional families produce functional children.**

Decision-making

If we are in a profession or in a business our mind is usually well trained to take professional or business decisions. We can do so because we are emotionally detached from the kind of work we do. **If we**

become attached to our work or our profession, we tend to over-work, over-exert ourselves and get over-involved in our jobs. Once again it is a sign of emotional insecurity. People who are good at making decisions in their business lives, when under stress, have great difficulty taking decisions in their personal lives. Such people may achieve a lot in terms of wealth and social status but they are not as successful at achieving their own happiness. **A happy individual can take even difficult decisions quickly. An unhappy individual will often take a long time to take very simple decisions.**

> *An elderly professor, who was a distinguished man in his own field, wanted to seek help for his panic attacks, fears and phobias. He was under such stress when he came in to seek therapy that it took him many weeks to decide his goals in therapy. He even found it difficult to decide whether he wanted to continue or discontinue therapy. Eventually, he dropped out after only a few sessions.*

Stress colours our decision-making. It makes our perception and our thinking hazy. **Confusion is an appropriate and healthy state of stress. When a person is confused, it means that they are in the process of changing or are ready to change.** Highly stressed individuals can be in denial of their problems. The decisions that people take when in a state of denial are quite different from those taken when the individual is free of stress.

> *A lady who was on antidepressant treatment was having difficulty deciding whether she should leave her husband. This lady had a heavy emotional baggage from her early years. When she started therapy, she was advised to refrain from making any decisions during the process of therapeutic change. She could take any decision that she wanted to once she finished therapy. Before her therapy started, she was of the opinion that it would be in her best interests to leave her husband. She finished her therapy successfully over the next few weeks. By this time she was able to deal with her marital problems successfully. She was happier than before. She eventually decided she could continue to live with her husband happily.*

Corruption

According to Abraham Maslow, our physical needs, like our needs for food and water, are our primary needs. These needs must be met if we are to physically survive. Once these needs are met, we grow mentally and we develop new needs. The highest level of need is the spiritual need.

When our physical survival is threatened, our mind perceives it as a stressful situation. It is the perception of threat that is the key to our thinking. There is hardly any need for the real threat to be there. During this state of stress, we unconsciously want to take control of our lives. We lose trust in our justice system, in other people and in Nature generally. We then want to do everything possible to ensure our own survival, disregarding others. This makes us selfish and self-centred. We become corrupt. This leads to lawlessness. We enter into the cycle of stress leading to corruption.

This cycle can be stopped at any point to lead to prosperity and happiness for everyone.

In societies where there is an abundance of food and water and other basics for physical survival, there is less need for people to become corrupt. The justice system remains strong because people in general respect the laws of the land. They have more trust in the 'system'. People feel more secure, in general.

There are many methods that governments can use to curb corruption. The most fundamental means of curbing corruption is to ensure the physical and mental security of all citizens. **Countries, like individuals, can be either stressed or de-stressed, depending on how secure their citizens feel.**

The Relationship Between Stress and De-stress

As I have said earlier, everything in Nature is relative. There is nothing that can be called absolute stress. Similarly, there is nothing that can be called absolute relaxation or an absolutely de-stressed state. For thousands of years, wise people have said that we owe it to ourselves to be happy. Nature has provided us with all the resources that we need to keep our life happy. Unhappiness comes in our lives at times when we lose someone near and dear. Even then, it is supposed to be transient. This is so because everything in life moves on. Our relatives, families and friends have all been described by philosophers as travellers who meet us during our journey of life. During this journey, we come from nowhere and we go into nowhere. Yet, for the time that we have to live in this world, we can choose to be happy or unhappy.

The responsibility for our happiness or unhappiness lies within our own selves. This might be a difficult statement to digest. At the end of the day, despite all the emotional and other problems that we have,

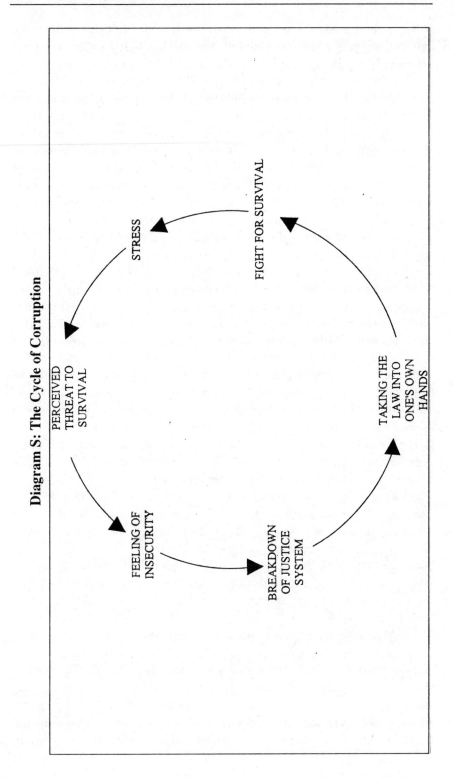

Diagram 5: The Cycle of Corruption

with the right guidance, we can come through our life's difficulties. We can become happy and contented within ourselves. The guides need not necessarily be therapists. They come in various hues and forms. They can be books. They can be experiences. They can be people. They can be religions. They can be religious leaders. We all decide for ourselves who is the right guide for us.

Stress is something that interferes in our moving towards happiness. We can only reach a de-stressed state by actively working towards it. Stress is the result of daily activities. A de-stressed state is the result of '*doing nothing*' physically and mentally for a few minutes every day. Stress is experienced at physical and mental levels. De-stress is also experienced physically and mentally. From Nature's point of view, once our physical and mental needs are fulfilled, we should be happy. If we are well-fed, well-protected and well-supported by family and society, we should ideally be happy. When everything is provided for by Nature, what reasons do we then have to feel threatened unnecessarily? If we are secure within ourselves, it gives us a sense of contentment and happiness. If we are happy, we are de-stressed. If we are unhappy, we suffer stress. Is it then a coincidence that people who are under stress find it hard to smile and that de-stressed people find it easy to laugh?

We live in a society that is becoming faster day by day. In order to follow the fast pace of life, we often become over-stimulated. Our nervous system gets heated up. It should then slow down, but we want it to maintain its fast pace to keep up with our pace of life. This state of mind is permissible if an individual is under threat because threats usually only last for a short period of time. But over-stimulation of the nervous system makes the mind pick up a message that we – as a whole – are under threat. Because mind and body are connected, this message is conveyed to the body as well. The body wants to keep pace with the mind and both of them, because they feel the threat, are put under stress. This inability to slow down, to stop, even for a short while, results in stress-related problems

> **FOOD FOR THOUGHT**
> **Behind every thought, behaviour or logic is usually an emotion.**

De-stressing ourselves is an active process. In order to de-stress ourselves we need to *actively* slow down. This means shutting our mind and our body for a short while every now and then. It is during this de-stressed phase that our mind recovers the energy that is lost during the stimulatory activity of day to day life. **We have to actively learn the skills to do nothing.** The amount of time required to clean up the impact of the environment on us depends on what kind of job we are in and what kind of stressful situations we are undergoing at any given moment. We need to learn the skills to de-stimulate ourselves on a regular basis.

Creating stress is a spontaneous, unconscious process. De-stressing oneself, on the other hand, is very much a conscious process. One has to learn skills in order to do this activity at an unconscious level. It looks like a paradox, and maybe it is. Skills of active relaxation are, unfortunately, missing in the modern educational system. These are skills that seem to have vanished from our religious learning as well. For example, confession was a regular de-stressing process that was practised for hundreds of years. As life has become more hectic, this activity has died down. The loss of such processes has contributed to an increasing number of people suffering from stress and stress-related disorders.

Stress is a condition of negativity. It makes us fall into a pattern of negative cycle. This cycle is self-perpetuating. One single factor or step in this cycle affects the next step. It is an ongoing, never-ending cycle. The ultimate aim of the stress cycle is to ensure the organism's survival by either fighting or running away. But if the cycle continues indefinitely, then the goal of the cycle is to let the organism die. After spending all its energy in fighting the threat, the organism will become exhausted and die.

But if we learn how to enter the cycle of de-stress, we experience positivity and happiness. This too is a self-perpetuating cycle. In order to move from a cycle of stress to a cycle of de-stress, some active effort is needed. To maintain the cycle of de-stress, we need to actively take time out to relax on a regular basis. Once we get into the habit of relaxing and de-stressing ourselves, life spontaneously becomes more positive and happier. It is also fascinating to see how many of the environmental factors that the individual previously thought to be out of his or her control, happen to work in the individual's favour. How this happens is something that we still have to learn about.

The more stressed a person becomes, the greater the chance that they may become physically and mentally ill. As a person becomes mentally ill, their life becomes out of control. The classic common factor among functional psychiatric illnesses is that a person becomes more and more focused on any *one* aspect of life's problems. All kinds of anxieties, phobias, depressions and psychoses have this common factor. The more the person becomes focused on only one aspect of life, the more that person becomes insecure and fearful; the more the person becomes insecure and fearful, the greater the chance of them becoming defensive. It is a well-known fact that on the rare occasions that a person suffering with schizophrenia attacks anyone, it is because they feel threatened. It is a form of self-defence that the person undertakes by attacking someone else. People who suffer from functional psychiatric illnesses are focused on *one* aspect of their own life that makes them feel insecure about themselves.

As the person becomes more and more de-stressed and relaxed the reverse starts to happen. A person becomes more and more self-confident and secure in their own self. A self-confident person has raised self-esteem.

As the person becomes de-stressed, the unconscious mind gets the message that the individual is safe and that life is happy. This message is conveyed to every organ in the body. The tension in every part of the body is removed. As the person becomes happier and more relaxed, the focus of attention shifts from the self to the surroundings and other people around the person. The person starts to grow intellectually. He or she starts to take a more active role in contributing positively to the lives of others. **The more de-stressed a person becomes, the more creative the person becomes.** People describe themselves as 'experiencing freedom', sometimes for the first time in their lives. It is a freedom of positivity, of optimism, of contributing constructively to society at large. A de-stressed individual spontaneously tends to respect nature and its laws, even without becoming aware of their existence. There is a spontaneous sense of self-respect and respect for others. Problem-solving and decision-making dramatically improve. The person becomes more comfortable with themselves and with others.

> **FOOD FOR THOUGHT**
> The moment we start expecting, our bodies and our minds get tensed up. This is a recipe for making our lives stressful.

The Words We Use

1. Stress Words

The words that we use during stress are also the ones that produce stress in us. 'No' is the first stress word that we learn, when we are small. Other words that we learn at an early stage are: 'don't', 'do', 'should', 'must', 'won't'. The mere mention of these words, even in a mild tone, brings about a sense of being stopped from doing something. They go against the flow. These words usually create stress when they are used. Often they are used in a forceful tone. For example, we might say, "I don't want to go there." The sentence is spoken in a tone of firmness and authority. We are stopping ourselves from going somewhere. There is a sense of mental rigidity in this sentence. Not only does this sentence create a stress in our physiology; it is usually said in a state of mind when we are under stress ourselves. Furthermore, it creates stress in the person who hears it. Any such word that has a negative connotation, especially when said authoritatively with inflexible rigidity, creates stress and comes from a stressed-out source. Obviously such words generate more and more stress.

2. De-stress Words

The words that de-stress or relax us are the words that we would usually use when we are in a relaxed framework of mind. 'Maybe', 'can', 'could', 'possibly', 'perhaps', are all relaxed words. The arousal levels of these words are low. They create a de-stressed state when used. They are less firm, less authoritarian than those listed above.

3. Neutral Words

These are the words that have ambiguous meanings depending on the person's state of mind. A person will pick up their meaning as stressful if they are under stress. Some of these words are 'God', 'Nature', 'death' and 'spirituality'. Depending on our state of mind at a given moment, we refer to these words in a positive or negative manner.

The content of our language reveals the state of our mind. Words that we speak and the words that we write reveal whether we are under stress or whether we are relaxed.

I have observed that, as there is an improvement in a patient's mental state, there is a change in the language that the patient uses. Patients may initially come to therapy with depressed states of mind. They use words of failure, of low self-esteem, of being angry with others, of being sad over losses. With progress in therapy, they become more and more accepting of their losses, more and more accepting of other people's drawbacks and they use more positive language.

> *A middle-aged lady who had problems with anger always found it difficult to cope with her mother. Her mother was an insecure, authoritarian and controlling individual who had seen a lot of financial hardship during the early years of her life. On finishing her therapy, the patient remarked "I know my mother cannot change, but I have become more accepting of her. I am at peace with myself."*

Advantages of Stress

Stress fulfils a role in our lives. It helps us to be ready to deal with danger. When a country is threatened by an external force, the whole population feels stress. The combat forces need this stress to fight the enemy. If the stress would be absent in such a case, the enemy would overrun the country without opposition.

Stress sometimes pushes us to create wealth for ourselves. Many rich people have generated wealth because they have felt insecure about themselves and money becomes their safety net. Stress gives such people strength to be on the go all the time. However, these people have to pay a price in terms of quality of life and freedom in order to seek elusive safety in wealth.

At a lower level of creativity, a stressful individual, especially one who is obsessive, would be a good worker on the factory floor. From a work perspective, this person would be a loyal, hard working individual without much creativity and with limited interests in life. **Stress makes us focused, narrow-minded, pushy, arrogant and stubborn.**

> *A young man, struggling to come to grips with his problems, realised that he held intense anger inside. He was encouraged to let go of the stressful anger. He refused to do so. He was prepared to continue to suffer because he also realised that his anger had enabled him to earn a lot of money.*

PART 3
THE DE-STRESSED STATE

6. LONG-TERM EFFECTS OF A DE-STRESSED STATE

A good example of a de-stressed state is hibernation. Certain animals can adapt to cold conditions by letting their body temperature drop to the level of the environmental temperature. As they become colder, their metabolisms slow down. They stop consuming food from external sources and use up food materials stored within their bodies. As they stop leading active lives, their need for energy falls. All of this ensures the basic survival of these animals. Once spring arrives, they come out of their hiding places and start to lead active lives. This raises their body temperature and they then need more food to match the increased energy requirement.

However, humans cannot hibernate. In fact, after being born, there is hardly any moment in our lives when the body and the mind are inactive at the same time. Even while we are asleep our minds are continuously working. Dreams result from these activities. Interestingly enough, we can actively learn how to hibernate.

'Relaxation' is a relative term. When we decide to relax, we decide to become inactive. This inactivity could be mental or it could be physical. Stopping ourselves mentally is one of the toughest (and paradoxically one of the easiest) of activities. Stopping ourselves physically is comparatively easy. Say for example, if we are working at a computer eight hours a day, our eyes and our brain tend to become tired. We can give a rest to our eyes, by doing a physical exercise. When we exercise, our sensation of touch is activated. When we take a break from one stimulus, we tend to compensate for this loss of stimulation by stimulating another sense. We get a temporary feeling of de-stress. In this case, we have rested our eyes to stimulate our sense of touch by just changing the focus of stimulation.

When we relax mentally, we can relax physically as well. This is because the mind and body are connected. However, it requires discipline to relax mentally on a regular basis because our mind is active most of the time. It is a storehouse of all the experiences, good or bad, that we have gone through. This storehouse is bubbling with activity all the time. In order to cool down those bubbles, we either have to let the steam escape or we have to engage in a more relaxing activity. Recently, neuroscientist Karl Pribram discovered that the frequency of vibration of the brain increases when we are most relaxed. Our brains seem to become more active, the more relaxed they become. Pribram was able to make this discovery using the Magnetic Resonance Imaging technique.

De-stressing ourselves is an active process, in which we make ourselves totally passive for a short time. This mental and physical passivity is just like the hibernation that animals go through.

Humans can actively become passive to create all the effects of hibernation. The more we de-stress ourselves, the more relaxed we become, and the less energy our body and our mind need to survive. **The less energy the body needs to survive, the fewer resources we require to live.** We require less food, less stimulation and less energy in order to accomplish more.

It looks paradoxical that we require less energy to achieve more. It is precisely this paradox that takes us into the realm of spirituality. **It's an old saying that the more relaxed we are, the more generous Nature becomes towards us.** Moreover, happiness *can* be achieved with wisdom and creativity.

FOOD FOR THOUGHT
We feel de-stressed only when our activities lead to relaxation of our nervous system.

Increased creativity is one of the most important effects of de-stressing oneself on a regular basis. **As we become more and more de-stressed, we develop an ability to solve difficult problems.** Our outlook and our perception towards problems start to become more positive and sometimes change dramatically. As we de-stress, the same problems that we found difficult to solve suddenly become easy to solve.

> *A young married man was referred by his general practitioner to seek help for panic attacks. These attacks seemed to occur at major points in his life. Such major points were always related to changes in jobs and he was at the time considering change of job. He was totally focused on 'the problem'. As a result, he had made himself so tense that he began to lose sleep and his appetite suffered. A week after our first session, as he continued to de-stress himself regularly, he became able to decide what he wanted to do about his job situation. It became clearer to him what he actually wanted in life. After two weeks he had taken his decision about his job and he was happy about it.*

Achieving a de-stressed state is a continuous process. Many people believe that they need to practice relaxation techniques only for the duration of their therapy. This is a fallacy. Because relaxation is a state of mind and body that we have control over, it is we who are responsible for putting ourselves in that state. The job of a therapist is confined to enabling the clients to develop skills to deal with life's situations, at a particular moment in time, when the help is needed. It is totally our responsibility, as patients or clients, to make sure that we learn the skills to de-stress ourselves on a regular basis, so that we can continue to maintain our creativity and develop our problem-solving skills ourselves. It is fascinating to watch someone who initially presents with low self-esteem work through their problems and become more and more de-stressed. The person spontaneously becomes more self-sufficient and creative and is in control of their life.

Achieving a de-stressed state, both mentally and physically, is a continuous life-long process. We can all develop within ourselves this ability to remain relaxed.

Accumulated Effects

The achievement of a de-stressed state is the result of an accumulated process. The more de-stressed and relaxed we are, the more abilities we tend to be able to exploit. Many people believe that others, e.g. family members, employers or colleagues, are responsible for their state of mind. One of the characteristic signs of a person becoming more relaxed is the sense of responsibility they tend to develop towards themselves.

> *A middle-aged man was referred for treatment following his depression. He had given up on living. He blamed his problems on one of his close relatives, who he said had emotionally abused him. By the time his therapy ended a few weeks later, he stated that he had realised that the total responsibility of his well being was his and his alone. He acknowledged that he had learned that working on himself was a continuous regular process.*

Spirituality and the De-stressed State

One of the fascinating aspects of the de-stressed state is that people begin looking at the spiritual aspect of life. It is also interesting to note that as a person becomes more and more de-stressed and relaxed, the fact that a person belongs to a particular religion, such as Christianity or Hinduism or Islam, becomes insignificant. The values that a person seems to develop spontaneously come through self-realisation. This self-realisation follows regular work with oneself, with one's emotions and with one's stressors. At the end of it all, as people de-stress themselves, common human values that transcend religion seem to start emerging. Interestingly, these values are without any of the dogmas that we see attached to many religious beliefs. The more the person becomes de-stressed, the more secure the person becomes within him or herself. The more a person becomes secure within him or herself, the more the person learns and experiences to trust Nature.

Acceptance

As a person becomes more relaxed, he or she becomes more accepting of self and others. 'To be', is a state of acceptance of what exists here and now. It is an acknowledgement of the ability to accept other people as they are and respecting them for what they are. It also means an acceptance of him or her self. A de-stressed person becomes more and more accepting of his or her own trivialities and frailties. **Because of this acceptance, a de-stressed person realises that all people are unique and yet are all part of the same universal whole.**

Open-mindedness

As we become more relaxed, we become more open-minded and more curious. When we work at active relaxation, we tend to realise how little we know about ourselves and the universe at large. Such a person becomes more receptive to new ideas. As people become more open-minded, they discover how ignorant they are of life in general. Once a person starts practising active relaxation, a person starts moving towards what Buddhists would call Nirvana, a state of perpetual bliss. Nirvana is a state of mind when the human body is free of all pains, illnesses and lust. The mind is free of any temptations and negative feelings. Physical and mental needs diminish. Wants and desires spontaneously become minimal. Active relaxation opens up newer areas of learning. As needs, wants and negative feelings diminish, the mind becomes more positive. Understandably, the time and energy usually spent in basic survival is spared. This makes the mind more receptive to new learning experiences. One of the signs of a relaxed mind is the curiosity to learn and accept new knowledge readily.

Abundance

As a person becomes more de-stressed and relaxed, their physical and mental needs tend to diminish. There is less dependence upon external agents for happiness, such as cigarettes or drugs. **The less material needs a person has, the more a person tends to appreciate the abun-**

dance that he or she lives in. This sense of having abundance provides a person with a sense of contentment.

Another interesting point is that some patients I have observed have become more prosperous after undergoing therapy. Surprisingly, this prosperity followed the de-stressed. It seems that Nature came to their help materially. The same financial problems that they were unable to resolve before they came into therapy were resolved spontaneously without them making any effort. This happened when people actively worked to become more de-stressed.

Wisdom

Wisdom comes to a person who is relaxed. Wisdom is different from cleverness. Both cleverness and wisdom require innate intelligence. Wisdom usually brings benefits for everyone around us. It enables a person to see things in a broad perspective. Signs of wisdom are looking at all angles of a situation or a problem quickly and taking into consideration all aspects of a problem so that the maximum number of people benefit. Wisdom comes to those people who work on themselves. The more de-stressed people become, the more worldly wise they become. Wise people can use their life experiences in order to solve problems in all aspects of life in creative ways. **Wisdom involves lateral thinking.**

Self-discipline

Self-discipline is important for the personal and professional growth of any person or organisation. The more de-stressed a person becomes, the more self-discipline they have. They do not need to make much effort to discipline themselves as their lifestyle is quite regular. The de-stressed person looks after themselves and does their duty towards family and society. Self-discipline comes into a de-stressed person naturally.

Freedom of Spirit

> *A young woman, who felt anger towards her father, under-went anger management. After the session was over, she was asked to comment on her experiences in the session. She shrugged her shoulders and expressed amazement at what she felt. "I feel so free," she said.*

In the above example, the young woman's body became de-stressed as her mind became more relaxed. Most people who finish therapy become free of both mental and physical tensions. They feel freer in mind and spirit. The more de-stressed one becomes, the freer one feels.

The freer one feels, the more choices one has in life. The more choices one has the more control one can have over one's life. Freedom of spirit is one of the long-term effects of maintaining a de-stressed state.

Adaptability

As we become more de-stressed, our ability to adapt to a new environment and new surroundings becomes better. We can adapt quickly to newer situations in life, changes that occur around us, any environmental or situational change, which, as a norm, is stressful. **Better adaptability is the result of more tolerance.** Recent research in blood biochemistry has revealed that people who have higher levels of the stress hormone, cortisol, in their bloodstream have a greater chance of developing post-traumatic stress when trauma strikes. From a clinical point of view, as patients let go of their negative emotions, their bodies and minds tend to become less excited in an environment, which before they would have found hostile. Even if their environment remains hostile, they develop a tolerance of it as they de-stress.

Humility

As we become more relaxed we tend to become more 'grounded'. People somehow become more humble as they experience a decrease in stress and an increase in relaxation. We have more appreciation and acceptance of what Nature has already provided to us. We tend to develop a sense of humility as individualistic ego boundaries diminish. Interestingly, the individual retains a sense of uniqueness while developing a sense of being part of a universal whole. This sense of wholeness, besides giving one inner strength, makes one aware of one's existence as a small component in the universal cogwheel. Interestingly, this process enhances one's self-confidence rather than diminishing one's self-worth. A de-stressed person becomes simultaneously more humble and more aware of being individualistically unique, of being a part of Nature.

Physical and Mental Health

One of the reasons that de-stressing techniques have recently become more popular has been because of their effects on the physical and mental well-being of the person. Recent decades have seen a mushrooming of alternative and complementary medical practices in the West. For example, yoga has been known to cause beneficial effects in physical and mental health for many centuries. In the West, yoga has been used exclusively for its health benefits. In India, yoga is practised as a spiritual exercise. Yoga is another example of how de-stressing techniques tend to overlap with spirituality. Physical and mental health are mentioned in Hindu and Vedic literature as by-products of higher spiritual goals.

Most complementary and alternative therapies emphasise the importance of relaxation. Most of them use relaxation in one form or another to achieve a beneficial outcome. Just because we have yet to scientifically validate the outcome of health effects of de-stress techniques, it is a matter of conjecture if people are going to wait for another few decades till, we can scientifically confirm that these techniques work. Some psychiatrists in the West believe that 'mental health' has yet to be discovered. The term 'mental health' is only understood in the context of 'mental illness'. Some people do not believe that mental health can be achieved through mental exercises in the same way as physical health can be achieved through physical exercises. There is also an erroneous belief that 'mental health' cannot be achieved without psychiatric help, which mostly involves pharmacotherapy. 'Mental health' is a state of balance that can be maintained by practising 'active relaxation'.

Optimism and Positive Thinking

A de-stressed individual is optimistic. A person who is de-stressed has a positive outlook on life. The de-stressed person lives in the 'here and now'. This 'here and now' approach allows people to spontaneously accept whatever has happened in the past and helps them to accept what is going to happen in the future. The more relaxed a person becomes through the continuous use of de-stressing techniques, the more optimistic they become. The same rule also applies to systems, such as organisations, families or groups of individuals working together to achieve a common goal. On the other hand, a person or a system under stress is usually pessimistic about the future and critical of the past.

Growth

A de-stressed individual, system, or society tends to move spontaneously towards growth. Everything in the universe is moving. Movement and transience of everything are laws of Nature. Everything in Nature also follows the law of least effort. This law states that we need only apply as much effort as is needed to fulfil a particular objective. The remaining effort then can be used to propel all relaxed systems or individuals towards growth. This growth can be financial, physical or spiritual. Growth generates abundance and a feeling of generosity. When a relaxed system helps people to grow individually and as a society, people spontaneously come to have enough materially to satisfy their day to day needs. This in turn makes them become more generous and charitable towards others. 'Giving away' in a sense also means 'letting go'. People who are relaxed and who can maintain growth also find it easier to 'let go'. Such de-stressed people are so generous that they can easily let go of their negative emotions and money in charity.

Slowed Ageing

Ageing is a natural process. Every living organism ages. Even civilisations age and die out. Although ageing is inevitable, stress and relaxation can affect the rate at which it occurs.

Many decades ago, experiments done with lab mice had shown that the ones who were fed little, remained thin, matured later and became older later. This was in contrast to the other group of mice that were fed more, became obese, matured earlier and aged faster. These experiments provided evidence of how increased metabolic activity caused mice to age faster.

However, recent work done by endocrinologists has suggested that a chemical named DHEA (dehydroepiandrosterone) is responsible for keeping us younger. As we age, there is a successive reduction of this chemical in our body. Normally, this chemical is produced naturally in all of us. Yoga and meditation (and prayer, probably) are supposed to discourage the reduction of DHEA in our bodies.

Practically all de-stressing techniques, including yoga and meditation, slow down the heart rate and lessen blood pressure. People who practise these techniques may also reduce their food intake. Although there have been few scientific studies done yet, there is an extremely good possibility that yoga, meditation and other de-stressing techniques reduce metabolic activity. Such studies would explain theoretically how de-stressing techniques could slow ageing and the reduction of DHEA in our blood.

Vedic literature mentions that it is possible for an average human being to have a lifespan of a few hundred years. This may seem incredible. However, if we are trained to reduce our metabolic activity on a regular basis, it is possible to increase our lifespan.

Signs of a De-stressed State

We can be more relaxed or less stressed. We can be more under stress or less relaxed. A de-stressed individual has the following characteristics.
1. **Work and Family**
   A relaxed individual can find a balance at work and in family life. Research conducted in the United States many years ago found that

business executives who had happy family lives performed well in their work.

2. **Time**

   One of the most important aspects of a relaxed individual is the respect that they give to time. Everything in Nature has a pace at which things happen. A relaxed individual works with that pace. Even if the pace needs to be increased for a short while, the relaxed individual slows himself and paces himself according to the demands of nature.

3. **Tone**

   A relaxed person has a slow, soft tone of voice. The tone is neither harsh nor too soft to be completely inaudible.

4. **Living in the Present**

   A de-stressed individual lives *now*. *Now* is what life is all about. The past is gone the future we do not know about. A de-stressed individual spontaneously lives in *now*.

5. **Security**

   A secure person is relaxed and a relaxed person is secure.

6. **Speed**

   Nature operates at a certain pace. A person who accepts and respects this flow of time can remain relaxed. Making life too slow is also an indication of unhappiness. An optimum speed of life is necessary to live comfortably. On occasions the speed of life can become fast, but it is necessary to slow it down again so that life flows comfortably.

7. **Focus**

   A relaxed individual finds it easier to change their focus from one subject to another. Developing the ability to do this is an important aspect of de-stressing ourselves. Going with the flow means being able to de-focus as we move from one aspect of life to the other. It happens spontaneously as we go with the flow. Distraction is slightly different. When a person's attention can be distracted very quickly, it is a sign of impaired concentration. However, the ability to change focus from one topic and to move on to the next is a de-stressing technique.

8. **Decision-making**

   We have to make decisions at every step in life. It is only as time goes by that we can determine the correctness or incorrectness of these decisions. When in a position where they need to take a decision, a de-stressed individual can easily and spontaneously look at the whole picture and take the right decision. On the other hand, decisions that are taken hastily under stress are more likely to be bad decisions.

9. **Money**

For many stressed people, money offers a safety net. Money acts like a surrogate parent that can provide them with love and affection and care. De-stressed individuals, on the other hand, regard money as a tool with which one can make one's life more comfortable. The more relaxed a person is, the less importance they give to money. For a de-stressed individual, money is just a medium for living life.

10. **Power**

Power is equal to service. This is the equation of Nature. The more de-stressed an individual becomes, the more power they have. The more de-stressed an individual becomes, the more service-orientated they become. A de-stressed person who gains the power of a public position is unlikely to become corrupt, as they are secure within themselves. Therefore, they use their power to provide service to people. A stressed individual who is given power will behave very differently. An insecure, highly stressed individual will use power to defend themselves against others. As a result, they will behave in an authoritarian and confrontational manner and will suppress others.

11. **Indulgence**

In the same way that a stressed person is over-indulgent, a de-stressed person finds that he or she has less physical needs. As one becomes more and more physically and mentally relaxed, one becomes less and less self-indulgent as regards physical needs and wants.

> *A middle-aged man found it difficult to cope with the fact that he was getting older. One of his major interests was over-indulging in sexual activities with younger women. As his emotional issues were resolved in therapy, he felt there was less and less need for him to continue these activities. There was a spontaneous willingness to spend his time in constructive activities.*

12. **Violence**

A de-stressed individual would use violence as a last resort in a hostile and dangerous situation. It would only be used when other avenues have been exhausted. In Nature, violence is the last resort. Diplomacy is an example of the kind of wisdom that says that violence is the last solution to a problem. Diplomats are supposed to be as relaxed as they can be even in hostile situations. This is because they can only work to postpone and hopefully avoid violence if they are in a de-stressed state.

13. Control

The more de-stressed a person becomes, the less that person wants to control things around them. It is a very interesting phenomenon, whereby a person acquires more control over events and their environment as they lose their desire to control these conditions. This phenomenon may seem paradoxical yet this 'easy control' is achievable.

> *An executive came into the therapist's office in a distraught state. He felt insulted at a board meeting because his immediate superior had reprimanded him in the presence of other members. He had decided that he was going to resign from his position. The therapist persuaded him to deal with the emotional issues in his life that were affecting his decision-making at that time. These issues were dealt with in a few minutes. Afterwards, the problems at his workplace sorted themselves out and the man continued to work in the same position. On one of his subsequent visits he remarked "My job seems to be perfectly under my control now. People seem to come to me now and ask me what I want. It is very different from before. I am not looking for control and I am totally in control."*

14. Selfishness

Selfishness is a sign of defensiveness or insecurity. A person who is under stress would be more insecure and defensive than a de-stressed individual. **The more physically and mentally relaxed a person becomes, the less selfish they become.** As a person develops a feeling of security, there is less and less need to hold on to anything and they can give to others physically and mentally.

15. Health

A de-stressed person is physically and mentally healthy. Yoga is well-known for creating physical and mental health. In ancient Vedic literature, yoga meant an alignment of body, mind and spirit. Ancient literature suggests that health is the first achievement of doing yoga regularly. Similarly, research on transcendental meditation has shown its effects in diminishing physical and mental stress. As our muscles become more and more relaxed, our blood vessels dilate to supply food materials and remove waste materials more efficiently. This is possible only in a relaxed framework of mind and body.

16. Emotional Arousal

Emotional arousal affects our nervous system and is caused when there is a disturbance to our mental equanimity. The extent of the arousal and our background determine what kind of activities we indulge in to counter this arousal. People develop various addictions and habits in order to diminish emotional arousal. Neuroscientists have discovered that people indulge in drug and alcohol addictions because they largely contribute to the secretion of dopamine in our nervous system. Dopamine is a neurotransmitter that is said to be responsible for providing a feeling of pleasure. This feeling of pleasure diminishes stressful emotional arousal. As our body and mind become de-stressed, there is less emotional arousal due to less secretion of stimulatory neurotransmitters. **Almost all habit and addictive disorders can be treated successfully if a person can be adequately de-stressed.**

17. **Values and Beliefs**

Our stressed state of mind distorts our value and belief systems. A child brought up in abusive conditions would usually tend to have a belief system that would encourage the child to inflict abuse on others. Alternatively, the child may be able to successfully experience a de-stressed state temporarily, following successful resistance to the abusive system. The more de-stressed a person becomes, the more positive their values and belief systems become.

> *An elderly single man, who had been through various forms of counselling and therapies over many years, was referred for his emotional problems. He had been brought up in an orphanage. During his time at the orphanage, he had witnessed other people being physically and emotionally abused. Although he was a highly intelligent individual, his beliefs about himself had determined that he was unworthy of even eating a regular breakfast or looking after his own personal needs. Despite being a successful businessman, he continued to deprive himself of food and proper living conditions. Within a few weeks of working with his emotional difficulties, his values and beliefs about himself changed dramatically. He bought a new house and a new car, revamped his business and started to eat well.*

18. **Telling the Truth**

Just as telling lies is a sign of fear and insecurity, telling the truth is a sign of confidence and self-assertiveness. **A state of mind in which a person feels comfortable with themselves without effort can be possible only if the mind is de-stressed.**

19. **Appropriate Stimulation**

Human life is a stimulating activity. Any form of stimulating activity usually produces heat energy. Without over-stimulating ourselves, we can consciously develop skills to become aware of the optimum stimulation for ourselves. The ability to maintain an optimum level of stimulation is a sign of a de-stressed individual.

20. **Ego**

Ego is the concept of individuality. 'I' determines our existence. When threatened, an individual or a group of individuals need to express their ego more aggressively. Membership of the human family subsumes an individual's ego so that the ego becomes less and less significant. The unconscious acceptance of this principle de-stresses us. The more secure we become in ourselves, the more humble we become. This humility leads us to become more aware of our part in the world's family and to look for more opportunities to provide service and to be generous to others. The more de-stressed we become, the smaller our ego becomes.

Rule of Thumb
'Try' to find happiness and it will evade you.
Do nothing and it will come to you.

---

7. ACHIEVING A DE-STRESSED STATE

Whenever any part of our body becomes diseased, our mind tends to perceive it through pain. Pain makes us aware that part of our body is unwell. The message of pain is conveyed to the brain. The brain gears up the rest of the body to work in unison to deal with this disease. Similarly, when there is tension in the nervous system, our internal organs respond to this tension. The existence of psychosomatic illness is evidence that our mind and body tend to work together. Therefore, if both the mind and the body are relaxed, then a person feels healthy and happy. This is another proof that both the body and the mind work with each other in harmony, influencing each other in a feedback mechanism. We can use this feedback mechanism to bring relief to the mind through relaxing the body. By relaxing the mind, we can also help relieve the body of stress.

Whenever the mind and the body perceive stress, a sense of turmoil tends to operate in the whole organism. This turmoil results in a nervous imbalance, which causes an imbalance in the organ systems of the body and increases tension in the muscles and the nerves. If this persists for a long time, the tension may become irreversible. When our body perceives stress, it also causes a disturbance in the autonomic nervous system. When we are healthy, inhibitory and stimulatory mechanisms of the autonomic nervous system tend to balance each other spontaneously. The stimulatory system prepares the body and the mind to work towards survival by either running away from or fighting the source of danger. The inhibitory system takes over the body mechanisms after the survival is ensured. The two systems need to balance each other by pulling at each other when one of the systems goes too far. A feedback mechanism operates here. The stimulatory part of the nervous system completes its role and then the other part, the inhibitory part of the autonomic nervous system, takes over. If however one of the stimulatory or the inhibitory systems persists in their activity for far too long, then the system gets tired. Sometimes this tiredness cannot be reversed easily. This causes an imbalance in the whole body. Illnesses, such as high blood pressure and peptic intestinal ulcers, are caused as a result of this imbalance.

Over-indulgence, over-activity, over-stimulation and over-inhibition are activities that cause stress. Our bodies and our minds have arbitrary limits of tolerance of an activity. Because each of us is unique, each of us has a different level of tolerance of a mental or a physical activity. Mental activities involve expenditure of a lot of energy. Even thinking, as a process, is an energy spending exercise. It is just like doing any physical exercise. An opposite trend to exercise would be physical and mental inactivity. A classical example of physical and mental inactivity is called 'psychomotor retardation', which is seen in depressive disorders. Though a person may be mentally and physically slowed down, such occurrence of inactivity is usually preceded by a lot of energy spending (fighting) activity. This drains energy from the body. It results in psychomotor retardation.

A famous research report on schizophrenia published in 1976 by Vaughan and Leff concluded that when people who suffer from schizophrenia are stabilised with medication, there is an appropriate amount of stimulation that is healthy for schizophrenics. Under-stimulation or over-stimulation would cause a relapse of the illness. The results were the same even in patients who were not on anti-psychotic drugs. Over-stimulation and under-stimulation also creates stress in people who are healthy and are not suffering from any psychiatric illness. **Moderation is the key to a happy de-stressed physical and mental condition.**

> **FOOD FOR THOUGHT**
> **Acceptance of our ability to reach a goal makes the journey easy.**

Slowing Down and Stopping

When we become stressed, we become hyperactive. We also find that our mind tends to race when we are under stress. As we become mentally and physically worn out from over-activity, our bodies and our minds tend to become exhausted and slow down. **One of the principal keys to maintaining a de-stressed state is to carry out our day to day activities at an appropriate pace.** This 'appropriate' pace is relative. It is the pace that we can maintain in life, which is neither too fast nor too slow. It is difficult to maintain this pace all of the time. It is almost impossible to be consciously aware of one's pace all the time. Despite this difficulty, it is still possible to be unconsciously aware of one's own unique pace.

Another key to maintaining a de-stressed or relaxed state is to take occasional breaks, both mentally and physically. Some professions and lifestyles have a fast pace. Keeping a slow pace in such jobs is impossible. In such cases, we need to become aware of the limits when our minds and our bodies start to wear out. Before we start to become exhausted, we need to take a break and stop. It depends on one's individual personality how much of a break one should take.

Our personality depends on many factors. The way we have been brought up, our emotional baggage, our current circumstances and the demands of our current job are some of the factors on which the pace of our life depends. We have to learn, through experimenting with ourselves, the most appropriate time for which we need to stop and how frequently we need to take breaks. Because each of us is unique, our ways of handling stress are also unique to ourselves. A computer salesman may need to stop completely, physically and mentally, for fifteen minutes after every two or three hours. Another person with the same job could tolerate stress for more than an hour and may only need a ten-minute break or a five-minute break each hour. This could, of course, be impractical. But this is where our wisdom and problem-solving come into play. These salesmen need to learn from their own personal experiences how they can perform their best. They can only learn through experiment how much time they need to spend on themselves and how frequently they need to actively de-stress themselves.

It needs to be emphasised here that when we talk of 'stopping' – it means 'completely' stopping the mind and body together at the same time. Simply taking time off routine work can help a person to a certain extent, but it is less rewarding than letting the mind and the body stop simultaneously.

Resources for De-stressing

We usually tend to find relaxation in various activities. Each of us will relax in a different way. The methods that we use individually to relax could be different, but they have the same outcome – a balance in the systems of our bodies. A feeling of relaxation gives us relief and a sense of contentment. After de-stressing ourselves, we say we feel 'refreshed'.

It is a fascinating fact that we are drawn spontaneously towards activities that would undo our experience of stress. This can be done by either 'overcoming' or 'diminishing' stress. Most of the activities that diminish stress would involve changing something outside of us in our environment. We also tend spontaneously to undertake activities within ourselves to 'fight' or 'overcome' stress without being aware of such activities. Examples of such 'stress overcoming' activities are smoking tobacco or drinking coffee, tea or cola drinks.

Exposure to Long-term Stress

When under stress, we usually tend to change our external environment. Such a change is healthy and invigorating. We temporarily change our place of living. Going on holidays is an example of such a change. We may also change our job if we find we have difficulty coping with it. If we have difficulties with our families, some of us may decide to leave them alone for a while. These changes tend to give us mental relief. However, such changes are useless if long-term stress leads to problems that are difficult to resolve. At such moments in life, we need creativity and wisdom to help us to sort things out.

Exposure to Short-term Stress

In dealing with short-term stress, we usually tend to take short-term measures. Invariably we turn to something stimulating that helps us to overcome stress. We may tend to smoke or we may drink stimulants like tea, coffee or cola drinks. We also drink alcohol to relieve ourselves of short-term stress. Regular physical exercise also helps us to deal with short-term stress. These examples show that we spontaneously tend to make changes within ourselves – in our bodies and minds – to feel more relaxed. Overdoing most of these relaxation techniques makes us addicted to them. **Addictions are the result of overdoing short-term relaxation techniques.**

The common feature of all these relaxation techniques is that all of them mean engaging ourselves to bring about a change in either our external environment or in our internal environment. Change is the law of nature. As everything is temporary and must move on, we need to move on in life, that helps us to deal with any situation that causes stress. How we move on and change the stressors – depends on the skills we acquire individually within ourselves.

The Active Process

Every technique for de-stressing ourselves involves an active process. We *have* to actively take responsibility for performing relaxation techniques in one form or another. If we fail to do that, then natural forces will force us somehow to take a break anyway when we get exhausted. This is the reason why people suffer with stress-related illnesses. After we have ignored the initial signs of stress, our bodies and our minds are brought to the point of exhaustion.

Wise people have used a term called 'actively passive'. It means that we need to 'actively' engage in 'passive activities'. Our unconscious mind is 'active' all the time, even when we are sleeping. It gets hardly any rest. We need to 'actively' allow it to rest, by being mentally and physically passive, for even a short time each day. Otherwise, we tend to unconsciously engage ourselves 'actively' in 'active' (stimulatory) processes, 24 hours of the day. When we smoke or when we consume much tea or coffee, we stimulate ourselves. **Tobacco smoke contains nicotine, which is a stimulant. Tea and coffee contain caffeine, which is another stimulant. When we are already aroused and stimulated with stress, we over-stimulate ourselves by consuming these drugs.** We then make ourselves 'actively active' trying to deal with our stress. On the other hand what we need on such occasions of stress is mental and physical passivity.

It is because of this need for being 'actively passive' that holidays can be rejuvenating. They can be productive only if there is least stimulation of the body and the mind. But if we can shut off our mind and our body for a short period of time everyday, we can de-stress ourselves easily making our life richer in all aspects.

Having a Holiday Every Day of our Lives

There are many books already written on stress management. Many techniques of stress management have been written and described in these publications. However, if we knew where stress comes from and why we are under stress at any given moment in our life, it would allow us to work on ourselves and provide us with more control in our lives. We can develop our own stress management techniques. We can be our own stress managers.

We may either fight to control our life or control it easily. In order to control our life easily, we need knowledge and the wisdom to apply that knowledge. **Nature's laws can be bent, but they cannot be broken. We need to learn to work around them rather than against them.** One of the reasons that we find stress all around us is because many people are working against the laws of Nature. Working with these laws and modulating them to our own needs not only de-stresses us, it also brings us happiness, creativity and prosperity.

Let us Try an Exercise

Make yourself comfortable sitting on any chair or lying down flat on your back. Close your eyes and allow your mind to go blank. As your mind becomes empty of thoughts, allow it to wander away to a beach that you might have visited or would like to visit. Allow yourself to lie on the sand on the beach. Imagine yourself feeling the temperature of the sand below you. Allow yourself to become aware of the warmth of the sun as you imagine yourself lying on the beach. Imagine yourself becoming aware of a soft breeze blowing on the beach. Imagine hearing the sound of sea waves as they strike against the shore. Imagine staying on the beach for the next five to ten minutes. Then open your eyes.

Most of the people who will undergo this exercise will feel refreshed after five to ten minutes. People whose bodies are tensed up to such an extent that easing the tension in their body would release underlying emotions may feel uneasy after doing this exercise. For others who are less tense, this experience could be like going on a holiday for a few minutes. By doing similar exercises regularly, the tensions in our bodies and our minds will be relieved and we can maintain a prolonged state of de-stress.

A De-stressed State in an Individual and a System

There are universal laws that operate at many levels. The same laws operate at the level of the universe and the same laws operate at the cellular level. Any individual when undergoing strain would eventually experience physical or mental breakdown. Any system that undergoes strain also has the possibility of eventually breaking down. Family therapists are aware that when any family undergoes extreme strain due to any particular member of the family, the family feels threatened. This threat is stressful. Such stress when prolonged results in the breakdown of the family. Similar principles can be applied to a country or society. 'Going with the flow' has been the password of relaxation and de-stress over the last decade. Wise people since time immemorial have known this phrase in various forms. It is another interpretation of how Natural laws need to be followed and respected.

In philosophy and spirituality, we learn that all of us are small parts of a universal whole. We find it difficult to comprehend that there could exist a common energy source – which some of us call God. Some of us find it difficult to accept that we are all part and parcel of a being called God.

Each human body is made up of trillions of cells. These cells include red blood cells, white blood cells, nerve cells, liver cells, bone cells and muscle cells. All these cells and tissues make us an individual, a complete whole. However, when we look at ourselves, we are unaware of trillions of these cells that make us an individual. When an individual body dies, it also kills all these members in the body. When a part of our body such as an organ made up of millions of cells, suffers with

FOOD FOR THOUGHT
Competing with ourselves is far more destressing than competing with others.

a disease, our whole body suffers. When we give charity with our hand, millions of cells of the hand co-ordinate with a decision that cells in the brain have undertaken. The credit for the act of charity goes to us individually rather than to the hand that gave it or the mind that initially took the decision. At the end of the day, in every form of life, the same universal system operates. Similarly when any system undergoes stress or strain, the same universal laws are broken. Respecting those laws nurtures an individual, a society, a country and humanity at large.

The Basis of De-stressing Techniques

All techniques for de-stressing oneself, at the individual, corporate or national level involve one or more of three methods. These methods are:
1. Addition.
2. Subtraction
3. Reorganisation of resources or internal management

1. **Addition.** Something is added to the system. For example, when more oxygen is added into the circulating blood by the inhalation of pure oxygen, mental and physical stress is reduced. Similarly, businesses and companies have sometimes to bring in someone with outside experience to bring about better work techniques, a move that can affect stress positively as well as negatively.

2. **Subtraction.** The removal of substances from the body or the removal of individuals from organisations. The removal of carbon dioxide and other waste products from the body can de-stress the body. Similarly, officials in the corporate or government levels are sometimes removed from their posts in order to de-stress the system.

3. **Reorganisation of resources.** This method of managing stress involves managing resources already available. By creatively managing already available resources, we can reduce stress. For example, the kind of foods that we eat, or physical exercise, can de-stress our body. We can organise the quality and quantity of food that we eat and organise time spent in physical exercise more efficiently to get better results. A business, for instance, can reorganise itself – making more efficient use of resources to de-stress itself.

De-stressing can involve all of the above three processes. When a company is under stress (threat of closure), the *addition* of a decision-maker at the top would be sometimes the first step. This person may decide to cut down on staff, which would be a process of *subtraction*. This then may lead to the *reorganisation* of resources, which may involve reorganising finances or personnel or work practices.

How Physical Exercise Reduces Individual Stress

Physical exercise involves the activity of a group of muscles in the body. It causes an increase in the metabolic activity of these muscles. Increased metabolic activity leads to a demand for a rapid supply of oxygen and food supplies to these muscles (*addition*) and a rapid elimination (*subtraction*) of waste products. In order to do this, the blood vessels have to work to their maximum ability. It means they have to expand to facilitate blood to move rapidly in the exercised area (*reorganisation*). For this sequence to be complete, our hearts beat faster and our breathing becomes deeper.

The holistic effect of physical exercise is shown by the fact that with greater oxygen intake and faster removal of waste products, the brain becomes more active. Brain cells are extremely sensitive to the presence of oxygen, food and chemicals. With the heart pumping blood more efficiently, brain tends to benefit from any form of physical activity. Physical exercise also tends to help release emotions locked up in the body systems.

The Role of the Senses

We have five senses: sight, smell, taste, hearing and touch. These five senses collect information from the environment and convey messages to the nervous system. The messages are conveyed either to the spinal chord from where they are conveyed to the brain, or the messages are directly conveyed to the brain through our sense organs. The brain and the rest of the nervous system pick up these messages, interpret them and decide how to respond. These messages are then conveyed back to the various muscles of our body. In the interaction between the senses and the nervous system, another system acts as a mediator. This is the endocrine system. The endocrine system secretes hormones that help the nervous system co-ordinate various body activities. These hormones are also responsible for emotional arousal. Once again, there is interplay between the endocrine system and the nervous system. The endocrine system affects the nervous system and the nervous system affects the endocrine system. When our senses sense a stimulus from the environment they convey the message to the nervous system. The nervous system then stimulates the endocrine system and hormones are secreted as a result. Inhibitory stimulation of the nervous system also affects the release of hormones. The endocrine system can also affect the nervous system in a feedback mechanism to stimulate its own inhibition. The emotions that we feel and all the accompanying problems and joys are the end results of these hormones. In the nervous system, the secretions that affect our mood state are called neurotransmitters.

Our Senses and the Stressed State

When a soldier is on the battlefield, all his senses are very sharp. Ready to fight, he has his ears listening to any changes in sound in the environment, his eyes probing, looking into the immediate vicinity all around, his nose smelling any change in the air, his skin sensing any change in air pressure, ready to fight for his survival. All his senses work actively, simultaneously conveying messages to the nervous system all the time. For the body and the mind, it is a highly stimulating situation. Most of the senses are actively engaged in ensuring that when the enemy strikes he is able to fight back successfully. During this process, body chemistry also plays a role. The endocrine system secretes noradrenaline, adrenaline and cortisol to the extent needed. Some neurotransmitters, such as serotonin, are blocked from being secreted. Serotonin would normally help the soldier sleep. But in danger this is one thing that he doesn't need.

Imagine a teenager watching a war movie on television or on a cinema screen. His eyes and his ears are stimulated due to incoming sound and the colours on the screen. Two senses – the senses of sight and of hearing – are stimulated excessively. Repetitive stimulation is conveyed to the nervous system and it is worked up. Repetitive excitement, without a break, irritates the nervous system. It perceives this over-stimulation as being stressful. (Try disturbing a teenager at the climax of a war movie, after an hour's viewing, and you will know what stress is all about.) These physical activities raise the level of stress hormones – noradrenaline, adrenaline and cortisol levels – within the body. The body and the mind – working together – do not know whether or not this threat is real. Unconsciously, the mind is totally unaware that the teenager is watching a movie. Although other senses like touch, taste or smell may not be involved in helping this teenager focus on the movie, the arousal level is of high intensity.

An executive is leaving home for work. It is early morning and he is late. He is a little bit cranky already because the night before was difficult for him. Because of this, he already has some anger in his system in the form of raised hormone levels. At normal levels, these same hormones would have helped him to deal with stress situations. Unfortunately for him, this morning, these very hormones are stimulating the nervous system to reach a stage until the feedback mechanism can take over or until he can express his emotions. When he doesn't find the outlet for expressing his emotions in the morning, he bottles it all up and

Diagram T: There is an order in the circularity of heavenly bodies - even their orbits are circular goes to his car to drive to work. This morning he drives fast, but feels that everyone on the road is a slow driver. He reaches his work in time, but decides against responding to the good morning wishes with which his subordinates address him. Today his eyes and his ears are going to make him experience what he does not want to experience – stress. Today his five senses will stimulate the nervous system more to continue to release more stress hormones.

The above examples indicates the ways in which our senses, our nervous system, our endocrine system and our neurotransmitters play their roles in creating stress.

Our Senses and the De-stressed State

The more senses that are stimulated at the same time, the more messages bombard the brain. This stimulates many areas of the nervous system. In addition, the pace of stimulation of all five senses contributes to increasing stress. Increased stimulation of the brain causes the brain to be overloaded with information. This prevents our nervous system from processing other incoming stimuli at the same time. The unconscious mind or the part of the nervous system that deals with emotions is called the limbic system. The limbic system has direct and indirect connections with all other parts of the nervous system. The more the limbic system is stimulated, the more stress hormones are secreted.

Once we realise the principle of how stress is created, we can work with our senses and our nervous system to create a de-stressed state in ourselves. Every phenomenon in Nature, whether it is a situation, an emotion or a physical state, has a beginning and an end. When stress caused by over-stimulation of our five senses and our nervous system continues indefinitely, the body starts to wear down. The body and the mind function together and behave as if the whole organism is in danger. When there is nothing else to fight, the body starts fighting itself. Once again, it follows from the laws of Nature that everything has to come to an end. The eventual outcome of chronic stress is death. This could be as a direct result of wear and tear through stress or through illnesses.

If we shut off any four of our senses and over-stimulate only one sense, then only one part of the nervous system is over–stimulated. When the four other senses are rested, then this particular sense, the fifth one, on continuous stimulation will eventually tire itself out. The part of the brain to which messages are being conveyed will also eventually tire out. As a result, there will be a spontaneous though temporary shut-down of this sense. An example of this phenomenon can be found in a common hypnotic exercise. This exercise requires a person to focus their sight on an object for a long time. To succeed, this exercise has to be done in a very quiet setting. When the setting is quiet, the sense of hearing is rested. If the person is sitting still in a smell-free environment without anything in their mouth, then their senses of touch, smell and taste are relaxed. If the person continues watching an object in this state for a long time, the muscles of the eyes become tired and the part of the brain that is over-stimulated by looking at the object also becomes tired. This makes a person feel relaxed and they close the eyes.

When we go in for a massage session – be it a head massage or body massage – it causes over-stimulation of the sense of touch. Most people go through the session with the eyes closed. During this time, the other senses are rested as well. Because only one sense is over-stimulated and this sense overloads only one part of the brain, the rest of the nervous system is rested and we feel relaxed.

The endocrine system and neurotransmitters also play a role here. When there is less stimulation from the external environment, there is less stimulation of the associated parts of the nervous system. This eases the endocrine system and the nervous system. The secretion of stress hormones is consequently diminished. Because the nervous system is also rested, the feedback mechanism working with the endocrine system ensures that it gets rested. It also affects the secretion of neurotransmitters. Neurotransmitters, like serotonin, are secreted more when a person is more relaxed.

The basic principle in the creation of a stressed state is that the greater the number of senses stimulated at the same time, the more the nervous system is stimulated. This causes stress, which is also caused and affected by the hormonal system in our body. The smaller the number of senses stimulated at the same time, the more we feel de-stressed. The moment the whole nervous system is shut down temporarily, all sensory input stops and we feel relaxed.

All forms of relaxation follow the above principle.

Shutting Down the Senses

There are various exercises and activities in this book that describe various methods to shut down the senses off and on to create relaxation. There are other exercises in the book that are also going to stimulate some senses and the nervous system. Once again, the principle behind the exercises is to overload one of the senses in such a way so as to cause over-stimulation of only a part of the brain or the nervous system. The de-stressed state can be achieved temporarily or on a long-term basis by regularly shutting down the nervous system and the senses. This can be done by various methods.

Economical Ways of De-stressing Ourselves

We can pay hundreds of thousands of pounds to de-stress ourselves or we can pay nothing to de-stress ourselves. At the end of the day, whatever we do, all de-stressing activities tend to have the same outcome. All de-stressing activities diminish our arousal level and cause a balance in the autonomic aspects of our nervous system. The autonomic nervous system is the part of the nervous system that is connected to the spinal chord and the brain and determines the activities of all our internal organs, including the heart, the stomach, the intestines, the bladder and the kidneys. This system is automatic. It is automatic because it is beyond conscious control. It is under the control of the unconscious. It is the limbic system – the emotional part of the brain – that deals with the unconscious. In all psychotherapies currently available, we positively affect this part of the brain either indirectly or directly. Through various methods of psychotherapy, we seem to achieve a balance – a stability – in this system. When this part of the nervous system is happy the whole nervous system is happy, the body is happy. The individual is happy as a result. A happy individual spreads happiness all around. The society at large, is affected by it. This shows how one responsible individual can create happiness around oneself.

> **FOOD FOR THOUGHT**
> If we are easy with ourselves, we can be easy with others.

We may go for holidays once a year or four times a year. We may participate in sand bath therapy or breath-work or take up Gestalt therapy or transpersonal therapy. All of these lead us to stability and equanimity creating a balance in our nervous system. The same effect can be achieved by many other activities. We may want to pray or meditate or to do nothing mentally and physically by lying down or sitting on a chair. All of these techniques will lead us eventually to the same outcome – relaxation. **In order to achieve happiness in life and physical health, all we have to do is: do nothing physically and mentally for a brief period every day regularly.** The more regularly we can engage in such activities, the shorter the duration for which we need to shut ourselves off from various stimuli to achieve the same results.

A busy executive spending half an hour every day doing nothing for brief periods, intermittently throughout the day, would be able to achieve far more than one who does not take time to de-stress. In such a scenario, the executive who does not de-stress would work themselves up each day, for many months, until it is time to take a holiday. If this holiday is deferred for too long, the resulting stress creates many other problems, which eventually lead to the person having to take more time off.

Dealing with External Stressors

A young, bright and beautiful woman, from a large family, was living with her family. She had been under so much stress that she had become depressed and suffered from low self-esteem. During this period, she started to focus more and more on her nose, which she felt was in some way crooked. She got an appointment for cosmetic surgery to be done on her nose and had drawn out money from a loan account to meet the expense. At this time she was referred for therapy. She was asked to move out of the house and start living on her own. She agreed to move out of the house and within weeks of moving, her depression lifted. She found a boyfriend. Her self-esteem was raised. She subsequently cancelled her appointment with the cosmetic surgeon.

This is a classic situation with which all psychiatrists are familiar. A change of external environment brings about a change in the person's stress levels. However, this is only one way to solve stress-related problems.

Dealing with Internal Stressors

A middle-aged working woman was suffering with anxiety. She had been anxious all her life. Recently, she had started to become more depressed, with diminished concentration, energy and ability to enjoy life. Although she was living separately from her mother with her only son, her mother seemed to rule her life. The mother was a domineering person. Her daughter had unexpressed and unresolved anger in her body systems. As she worked through her anger, the quality of her life started to change. Eventually, she looked at her mother in positive ways that she was never able to do before. She could see her mother's problems, her mother's inability to change herself and the suffering her mother had undergone herself. She could see that her mother had unresolved anger too. This lady was able to successfully solve the relationship problem between herself and her mother. This also positively affected her own job and her relationship with her own son.

This is another example of a person becoming de-stressed as the internal stressors are dealt with. As a person becomes more de-stressed inside, the 'rubbing' with the external environment tends to diminish. **No matter how hostile the environment, if the person is relaxed, their coping skills improve.**

Stress and the Law

The current legal system in the developed world is geared towards compensating individuals against external stressors, but these external stressors play a limited role in the stress a person feels. In other societies, which give too much responsibility to Nature, there tends to be a fatalistic approach towards life's problems. This makes many people passive, resulting in blaming either oneself or Nature for one's difficulties.

The legal system in both these societies would tend to look at stress and its related problems in quite different ways. The legal system in each society is geared towards the belief system that is prevalent in society at any given moment in time.

The Final Word

These words are probably the beginning of a new way of thinking about stress. The key to a de-stressed, happy lifestyle is balance in every aspect of our lives. We can achieve most of this balance by letting go of many things. To let go of anything, including emotions, means having confidence in oneself. This confidence comes from our childhood and the way in which we are reared. Once again it is a cyclical phenomenon. At each and every step of our lives, we have to balance and counter-balance events, situations and gains. Nature causes problems for us, but also provides solutions for these problems. We can find solutions by either fighting the problem or stopping to look at what is happening and then finding ways to deal with the problem. Whatever we might do, the end result is a balance. This balance can quickly become an imbalance. So we have to continue to maintain that balance throughout our lives. We can either decide to create this balance by fighting or we can decide to do it wisely. A wise option is to do things in a way that any decisions that we make in life benefit as many lives as possible. There are various ways and means by which we can solve our problems. The way that we solve our problems at any given moment in time depends on our own internal factors. **In dealing with situations, however logical we may be, there are emotional elements that affect our decisions and how we act on them.** Any decision taken by a person at any given moment in time is right. It is the consequences of the decision that determine whether the decision was right or wrong. There are, however, basic laws in Nature, which support any activity that promotes growth and universal well being. Any activity that leads to destruction or damage to self and others is against Nature. **We can deal with most of the adverse situations in life if we only know how to deal with stress.** Hopefully, this book will make us take more control of our lives easily without causing stress to ourselves and to others.

8. EXERCISES

This chapter describes seventeen simple exercises. These exercises have been clinically tested. Hundreds of people have benefited from them. The experience of doing them is intense. Regularly doing some of the exercises can bring calmness. Sometimes, just one exercise, when practised regularly, has the desired effect.

Caution is needed when following instructions. These exercises can arouse emotions. Therefore, people suffering from any physical condition, illness or disease that could become worse with emotional arousal should not do these exercises. If in doubt, you should contact your doctor.

Once the emotional arousal occurs, the exercises should be stopped. It may take a few days for the arousal levels to come down. Repeating the same exercise again after a few days then would usually be less arousing than before. Progress can be monitored.

These exercises will be helpful for normally healthy people who are looking for ways to deal with stress. Therapists may find them effective in bringing up blocked emotions in their clients. The last two exercises are metaphysical in nature. They reveal a hidden fact that the problems of stress can be made bigger or smaller. It depends on us, whether we consider the problems of stress all consuming or come to grips with them.

Exercise 1

Sit on a chair comfortably. Make sure your feet are on the ground and your backbone is straight and as comfortable as possible. Close your eyes. Just relax or do nothing.

Comments. Sometimes people will find this exercise sometimes difficult to do. People whose minds are racing and who are physically on the go all the time will find this exercise difficult to do. For others they can move on to Exercise 2.

Exercise 2

After sitting comfortably on the chair, close your eyes. Let any thoughts that come into your mind, come into your mind. Let the thoughts move on. The thoughts can come in only on the condition that they have to move on. Take your time, letting the thoughts come in and letting them move on. Continue doing this till all the thoughts have gone out of your mind and your mind becomes blank. Now look into that blankness.

Comments. Instead of 'fighting' the thoughts as we usually do or 'dwelling' on the thoughts, we let the thoughts come in and move on. This follows the law of Nature of letting things just happen. It surprises many people when they learn that they actually tend to have the blankness in their minds sooner than they thought they would.

Exercise 3

Close your eyes. Look into the blankness in front of your eyes. Now focus on your breathing. Allow yourself to become aware of your breathing. Take a deep breath. Give a brief pause. Breathe out slowly. Do it for one, two or three minutes. Then open your eyes.

Comments. This is the commonest exercise that most relaxation therapies tend to promote. Some yogic and meditational techniques also focus on breathing. Just doing this exercise can lower one's heart rate. This slows down the activities of other body organs as well.

Exercise 4

Close your eyes after making yourself comfortable on a chair. Focus on your breathing. Take a deep breath in. Give a pause. Breathe out slowly. Now count from one to five in your mind as you breathe in. Count as slowly from five to one as you breathe out. Continue breathing and counting for next few minutes. Spend one to five minutes, or more doing it.

Comments. This exercise is an advancement over the first three exercises. Controlling one's breathing, has been one of the oldest traditions of doing meditation. Once again this exercise slows down the body's physiological processes.

Exercise 5

Make yourself comfortable on a chair. Take a few moments to recognise the tension in your body. Now look into the blankness in front of your closed eyes. In your own mind, just scream. Continue screaming for five to ten minutes. Then stop. Make yourself comfortable again, with your eyes closed. Feel the tension in your body again.

Comments. The usual experience with this exercise is that the tension in the body tends to diminish. This exercise can be continued intermittently. If one continues to do this exercise regularly, after spending a few minutes everyday, a person could find that he or she is unable to scream further. In such cases there would be a dramatic release of tension from the body and the mind. Some people might find an increase in tension as they do the screaming exercise. This sometimes happens before the tension starts diminishing.

Exercise 6

Keep a glass of water or a bottle of water with you at all times. As you continue your day's work, take a sip from it regularly.

Comments. Regular intake of water, helps us to excrete metabolic products from our body. This diminishes the levels of toxic materials produced in our bodies that affect our mental state.

Exercise 7

Make yourself comfortable on the chair. Close your eyes. In your own mind, call out your name as fast as you can, as many times as you can, for next 60 to 90 seconds. Keep your eyes closed. Sense the feeling that you get now. Now call out your own name in your own mind as slowly as you can for the next 60 to 90 seconds. Stretch your name as long as you can each time. Keep your eyes closed. Now, sense how you feel in your body.

Comments. This exercise teaches us that when we tend to think very fast or do things very fast, we create stress. As we call out our own name slowly in our own mind, our whole body seems to follow that mental sound. This spontaneously creates a sense of relaxation throughout our body.

Exercise 8

Make yourself comfortable on a chair. Close your eyes. Now take a deep breath in and hold this breath for a while. Now start exhaling. As you exhale, call out your own name stretching it out in such a way that as you breathe out once you have called out your name once. Take as long a time as possible to call out your name as you exhale, stretching your breath. After doing it once, take your time getting your normal breath back, once again take a deep breath in and exhale out slowly calling out your name with each breath. Do it as many times as you can for about ten minutes.

Comments. This technique is a very powerful technique. Sometimes it can bring up a lot of underlying emotions. It is recommended only for those people who can tolerate strong emotions as they come up. This technique is like the chanting of a mantra.

Exercise 9

Seat yourself comfortably in a chair. Close your eyes. Allow your body to be as still as can be done. Now focus on your heartbeat. Allow yourself to become more aware of it. If you were to now wish it to slow down, within the next few seconds or so you may see the results.

Comments. This exercise is an example of how powerful our thoughts are. The trick of doing this exercise like all others is to do it 'easily'.

Exercise 10

Make yourself comfortable on the chair. Close your eyes. Now imagine seeing all the people who you think have played important roles in your life. Note their facial expressions.

Comments. This is an interesting exercise to become aware of our internal stressors. People that we imagine to be happy, contribute much less to our current stress, as compared to others who we imagine seeing angry or sad or hurt. It is almost impossible to change the image that one sees in imagination, by forcing ourselves to imagine differently.

Exercise 11

Close your eyes. Imagine seeing someone who has hurt you recently or with whom you have been angry recently. Notice the facial expressions on this person's face in imagination. Also allow yourself to become aware of how you feel imagining seeing this person in front of you. Now keeping your eyes closed and looking at this person in imagination, just scream in your own mind. Continue screaming for the next five minutes. After five minutes stop screaming in your mind. Keep your eyes closed. Take some deep breaths. Once again look at this person in imagination. You will notice a change in the facial expressions. Now notice the feeling that you have looking at this person.

Comments. This exercise teaches us the relationship between our perception and our thinking to the emotions that we carry about any particular event or person. As we release the emotion that we carry, the image changes. We ourselves become more comfortable.

Exercise 12

Make yourself comfortable on a chair with your backbone straight and comfortable. Imagine seeing the image of any person that you have been angry with. Imagine remembering the exact event or events with this person that make you feel angry. Now notice tension in any part of your body. This is possible to do with your eyes closed just imagining to scan your whole body. Now in your own mind scream at this person for the next five to ten minutes. Then stop screaming in your mind. Once again feel the tension in your body at the same place. You will notice a change.

Comments. Usually this exercise would ease the tension in that part of the body, which has been affected by anger. Sometimes this tension can increase as we do this exercise. During such times we simply need to continue this exercise on a more regular basis. This is especially true if anger has been aroused doing this exercise. If aroused and not released, it will continue to disturb your present life. Continue the exercise until you are comfortable.

Exercise 13

Make yourself sit comfortably on the chair, with your feet firmly on the ground. Close your eyes. Now think of any situation, or event in your life that could have been life threatening, or that aroused fear in your mind at that particular point in time. Even if you think it has been in the past, remember the whole sequence of this event please. Go through the event from the beginning to the end. Keeping your eyes closed, feel the sensations in your body. Recognise the feeling that you get in your mind.

Comments. This exercise will tell you if this event is still causing any problems in your present situation or not. Many times people suffer with post-traumatic stress. Many people fail to realise that this traumatic stress could be affecting their lives in subtle ways. Clearing up this stress would require therapy. Some of the exercises in this book could be helpful in diminishing stress related to such an event.

Exercise 14

Close your eyes. Make yourself comfortable in your chair or in your bed. Imagine looking at someone who had wronged you at some stage in your life but whom you think you have forgiven. Now look at the expression on this person's face. Become aware of how you feel looking at this person. Now go over to this person in imagination extending your hand to this person and saying to this person, I forgive you. Become aware of how you feel and what expression this person has on his or her face. Now let this person fade from your imagination. Now imagine looking at another person who has been helpful towards you. Look at the expression on this person's face. Become aware of your own feelings towards this person. Now imagine going over to this person and extending your hand to this person saying thank you and I forgive you. Look at this person's facial expression now. Become aware of your own feelings. Appreciate the difference that you notice in your responses to these two different people.

Comments. Forgiveness is a feeling of generosity. Forgiveness is a gesture that more powerful people can show to weaker ones. Simply saying or thinking that we have forgiven is sometimes insufficient. The emotions that we tend to carry within our own selves, with this unfinished business, is stressful for our bodies and our minds.

Exercise 15

Sit comfortably on a chair. Close your eyes. Let your mind be blank. In your mind, count from one to twenty-five slowly. Then open your eyes.

Comments. Just closing one's eyes can be relaxing for the mind. Counting keeps the mind from wandering away.

Exercise 16

Sit comfortably on a chair. Close your eyes. Let your mind go blank. Sit still in this position for next five minutes. Open your eyes.

Comments. Keeping the mind blank is the key to this exercise. The moment the mind goes blank, its connections with the rest of the body start easing. The body spontaneously becomes relaxed. It is a difficult exercise for someone who has heavy emotional baggage.

Exercise 17

Step 1 – Focus on the dark (black) spot in the centre of the big circle. As you look at it, become aware of the area around the black spot. Become aware of the boundary of the big circle, focusing on the black spot.

Step 2 – Focus on the black spot again in the centre of the big circle. Continue looking at it for the next few minutes, until you are aware of only the black spot. Everything around it will become hazy.

Comments:

Step 1 – It teaches us that we can continue to be aware of the whole picture, though looking at one spot – (dark spot in this picture).

Step 2 – The more we focus on the black spot – in our perception – it becomes bigger. We lose sight of the big circle around it.

Diagram U: Exercise No. 17

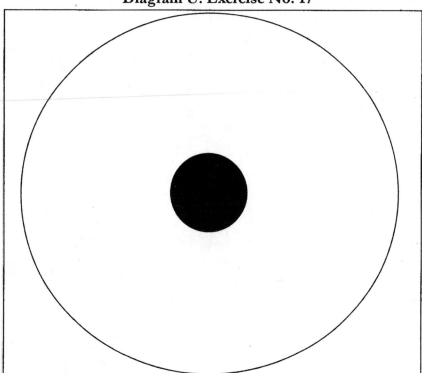

In life, we tend to do the same with our problems. We can keep them
small or make them big.

Bibliography

G Asaad, *Psychosomatic Disorders* (USA: Brunner/Mazel) 1996.

E Berne, *Transactional Analysis in Psychotherapy* (UK: Souvenir) 1961.

W B Canon, "Stresses and Strains of Homeostasis" *American Journal of Medical Sciences* (1935) No. 189.

D Chopra, *Ageless Body; Timeless Mind* (USA: Random House) 1991.

P Davies, *Superforce: The Search for a Grand Unified Theory of Nature* (USA: Simon & Schuster) 1984.

L Dossey, *Healing Words* (USA: Harper) 1993.

S Freud, *The Essentials of Psychoanalysis* (UK: Penguin) 1986.

D. Goleman, *Emotional Intelligence: why it can matter more than IQ* (Bloomsbury Publishing) 1996.

A C Guyton, *Human Physiology and Mechanisms of Disease* 3rd edn (USA: Philadelphia) 1992.

J A Hobson, *The Chemistry of Conscious States* (USA: Little Brown & Company) 1984.

M Kaku, *Hyperspace* (USA: Oxford University Press) 1994.

W R Lovallo, *Stress and Health* (USA: Sage Publications) 1997.

A H Maslow, *Motivation and Personality* (USA: Harper & Row) 1970.

I P Pavlov, *Lectures on Conditioned Reflexes* (USA: Liverlight) 1929.

C Pert, *Molecules of Emotion* (USA: Scribner) 1997.

E L Ross, *The Psychology of Mind-Body Healing* (USA: WW Norton & Company) 1993.

H Selye, *The Stress of Life* (USA: McGraw-Hill) 1956.

B F Skinner, "A Case History in Scientific Method" *American Psychologist* (1956) Vol. 11.

Lao Tzu, *The Tao Te Ching* (USA: Element) 1997.

C E Vaughn & J P Leff, "Influence of Family and Social Factors on the Course of Psychiatric Illnesses" *British Journal of Psychiatry* (1976) No. 129.

Index

A

Abuse, 80, 86, 87
Acceptance, 4, 106
Addiction, 80, 81, 82, 84
Affairs, 91, 92
Alcohol, 68, 70
Alcoholism, 21, 59
Anger, 29, 99
Anxiety, 65

B

Behaviour, 55, 56, 57
Berne, Eric, 74, 79
Bipolar affective disorder, 65
Blood pressure, 38, 44
Brain, 43, 60, 77
Buddha, 17

C

Cancer, 76
Cause and effect, 18
Conditioning, 49, 77
    Classical, 49
    Operant, 49
Control, 70, 113
Corruption, 93-95
Creativity, 47, 100, 103

D

Death, 18, 19

Decision-making, 69, 70, 80, 92, 93
Depression, 43, 57, 65. 97
Drug abuse, 59, 82–83

E

Eating disorders, 80, 81, 84-85
Ego, 70, 115
Einstein, Albert, 8
Emotional arousal, 84, 113
Emotions, 8, 27, 29, 39, 40, 55-57, 58, 59, 64, 66, 69, 72, 74, 75
Exhaustion, 42, 44, 61, 118

F

Family, 8, 61, 73, 80, 88, 89, 90, 92, 122
Fear, 29, 35, 57
Feedback mechanisms, 33-34, 37
Forgiveness, 27
Freud, Sigmund, 84
General Adaptation Syndrome, 41

G

Generosity, 29
Gita, Bhagwad, 18
Goleman, Daniel, 40
Government, 27, 61, 94

H
Habit disorders, 84
Hindu literature, 109
Hitler, Adolf, 12, 24
Holism, 25, 26
Hormones, 33, 124, 125

I
Indulgence, 112
Inertia, 16
Insecurity, 16, 69, 90, 91, 94
Islam, 69

J
Jesus Christ, 28

K
Karma, 18
Kelly, George, 75

L
Language
    And state of mind, 98-100
Law of conservation of energy,
    20
Law of conservation of matter,
    20
Laws of nature, 11, 65, 67
Lying, 72, 84

M
Medication, 68
Memory
    Effects of stress on, 76
Mental illness, 39, 40, 42, 65,
    80, 81
Mind-body connection, 52

N
Napoleon Bonaparte, 26

Natural catastrophes, 13, 42, 43
Natural phenomena, 5
Nervous system, 34, 35, 36, 37,
    43, 44, 58, 117, 124, 129
Neurosis, 58
Neurotransmitters, 38, 39, 128
Newton, Isaac, 8, 16, 64

O
Obsessions, 80, 87, 88
Obsessive-compulsive disorder,
    88
Open-mindedness, 106
Optimism, 109
Over-stimulation, 96

P
Pavlov, I P, 49
Perception, 55, 56, 57
Personality types, 59, 118
Pert, Candace, 59
Phobias, 65,77, 97
    And de-sensitisation
        techniques, 57
Physical exercise, 124
Physical illness, 27, 42, 80
Political fanaticism, 80, 90
Power, 70, 112
Pribram, Karl, 103
Psychiatry, 43, 44
Psychoses, 97
Psychosomatic illness, 80, 81,
    117
Psychotherapy, 8, 64, 65, 84

R
Racism, 91
Reich, Wilhelm, 52
Relativity, 51
Relaxation, 41, 56, 65, 97, 106,
    128, 129

Relaxation techniques, 83, 103, 119
Religions, 8
Religious fanaticism, 80, 90
Respect, 4, 5

S
Schizophrenia, 38, 65, 118
Selfishness, 70, 113
Selye, Hans, 41
Smoking, 82, 83, 121
Spirituality, 105, 122
Stimulation, 42, 43, 75, 115
Stressors
    External, 44, 45, 46, 47, 75, 83, 84, 91, 130
    Internal, 44, 45, 46, 47, 75, 91, 130

T
Tension, 52
Thinking, 55, 56, 57, 75
Transactional analysis, 74, 79

V
Values, 72, 114
Vedic literature, 10, 109, 110
Violence, 70, 112

W
Wave motion, 13
Wisdom, 107

Y
Yin and Yang, 12
Yoga, 108, 109